The Overcoming

The Overcoming

A story of resilience and
love after loss

Jacqueline Gaul

A catalogue record for this book is available from the National Library of Australia.

Trade Paperback ISBN: 978-0-6458993-2-0
eBook ISBN: 978-0-6458993-3-7

Print information available on the last page.

We at The Kind Press acknowledge that Aboriginal and Torres Strait Islander peoples are the Traditional Custodians and the first storytellers of the lands on which we live and work; and we pay our respects to Elders past and present.

THE
KIND
PRESS

www.thekindpress.com

To my living children,
may you live a courageous life.
I love you.

Contents

One

Trent

I remember the first time I saw him. I was attending a local college studying hospitality. Not knowing what I wanted to be when I grew up, I set off on another one of those adventures, seeking something to cure my boredom, keep my brain entertained, and move me forward in life. I have no idea why I was drawn to hospitality. I wouldn't be surprised if I chose this course because it's the cheapest and shortest on offer. Or perhaps it was the opportunity to meet new people, the desire to be of service, and most likely, the offer of free food from the trainee chefs in the test kitchen next door.

I'd had one hospitality job before college while I was still at school. I remember it well. I worked at a small local Chinese restaurant in the suburbs. From the outside, it looked like one of those places you think twice about entering—tucked away at the back of a small shopping complex, red and gold writing plastered all over the windows, creamy coloured lace curtains draped across the front, offering the smallest of glimpses inside. The restaurant was owned and run by a Chinese woman named Kitty and her husband, Charles. What I remember about Kitty is her strong work ethic and dedication to the customers she served. She was loved by so many and went above and beyond to offer the best experience for her customers. I loved learning this from her. She was also very generous with her staff, giving us lucky money on Chinese New Year and other special occasions. I think the idea is to keep the lucky money in the beautiful red envelope as a symbol of luck and prosperity, though I almost always spent it within a day or so. We worked hard in the restaurant and were often given big tips from the regular customers. Being the generous woman she was, Kitty never kept any of this money for herself, or the restaurant, and instead split it between the two waitstaff rostered on that evening. We were always grateful for this gesture.

I laugh as I remember some of the more quirky things about the place, like the doors being propped open by an unused roll of toilet paper. There was also the thing about my name. For whatever reason, Kitty refused to use my actual name when speaking to me. She'd ask me to take an order, or help with something in the restaurant, and instead of calling me by my real name, spelled out and displayed very clearly on my name badge, she opted to call me 'girl'. "Girl, do this. Girl, do that," she'd say. I'd often remind her of my name by showing her my badge, although it was never enough to convince her otherwise. For the duration of my tenure, I was known as 'girl'.

So here I was, drawn back to hospitality at college, not really knowing why, when he walked past and offered a smile. He was a handsome guy sporting the Queensland glow. You know that beautiful tanned skin, lovely eyes and gorgeous smile. He was a combination of surfer dude mixed with the classic Aussie tradesman. I could tell he was older than me just by looking at him, but by how much, I couldn't be sure. I also didn't know what meaning, if any, to make of the smile.

Week after week, we'd pass each other and share a customary smile as if in some kind of routine. I remember, one day, he was coming down the library stairs towards my friend and me. I felt nervous and began to have one of my nervous sweating episodes. He walked past, gave his usual smile as was customary and said,

"G'day mate". I remember thinking to myself at the time that we were in a total friend-zone situation as a single dude would never address a woman by referring to her as 'mate'. The polite g'days continued for some time until I found myself alone in the cafeteria one morning.

Quite often, I'd arrive early to college and would walk around, read a book, study or sip on a coffee. This one particular morning, I spotted him walking down the stairs, towards where I was sitting alone. Thoughts ran through my head as I grew nervous. I didn't have the safety net of my friends to fall into if my awkward self decided to pay a visit. I thought, *oh gosh, he is coming towards me. We are all alone. I am going to have to say hello.* I was blushing like a tray of overripe tomatoes and shedding beads of sweat as the nervous energy raced around my body. He seemed confident, walking right up to me as I sat alone at the table and introducing himself. It wouldn't come as a surprise to those who know me that I was so nervous I misheard him when he said his name and responded, "Oh Terry, nice to meet you." "No, it's Trent, actually," he replied. *Nailed it!*

He gave me his phone number. I am not sure if it was because he was as nervous as I was, or if he just didn't know the digits of his own phone number, but in that moment, he gave me the wrong combination of numbers. I waited a couple of days before attempting to contact him. Then I waited a few more days in anticipation of a reply. When it didn't come, I was confused as to what was going on. It would be a couple of weeks before I'd see him again, so I spent most of that time in a state of paranoia, questioning why he'd give me a bum steer and convincing myself that he definitely wasn't interested.

When I saw him next, I shared with him that I'd tried to contact him a few weeks prior but had heard nothing back. I told him I felt confused as to what was going on. He assured me it was an accident, and he just couldn't remember his mobile phone number as he rarely said it out loud to people.

Once we sorted the phone number saga and exchanged numbers for real, we organised to go out on a date. This was the first ever real date I had been on in my life. I was a ball of nervous and excited energy all rolled into one. I had no idea of first date etiquette. Then there were the finer details of what to wear and where we'd be going. The only thing Trent told me about the date was to bring an umbrella, which made me even more nervous about what we would be doing! He picked me up from my home, met my parents, and then we headed off in his little black work ute. He was wearing loafers, which my mum later commented on as being a bit weird.

First stop. Sushi. It was the first time I'd ever eaten sushi. A notoriously fussy eater, I hadn't tried many cuisines, other than the occasional Chinese. Even then, I only ever ate fried rice and spring rolls. We approached the train. I had no idea what to choose, so Trent took the lead, gathering a few plates for us to share. The moment I put the first piece of sushi into my mouth, it instantly triggered my gag reflex, and all I wanted to do was spit that bit of sushi out onto the plate. I tried desperately to play it cool, giving myself the pep talks: *You can do this, just chew it, and swallow it.* Gag. Gag. Gag.

My struggle didn't go unnoticed, and prompted by Trent's questions, I eventually came clean about my dislike for sushi. Shortly after, we headed into town and attended a night market by the Brisbane river—the reason why I needed an umbrella. By the time we had walked and talked, I was absolutely ravenous, so we stopped at a local takeaway and ordered some hot chips and gravy to satisfy my hunger. Job done.

As Trent and I chatted that night, I learned more about what he did. He was an electrician and former coffee roaster. He was attending TAFE to finish his electrical apprenticeship and was seven years my senior. Despite the age gap, we got along well, had lots in common, and enjoyed each other's company. Trent and I caught up a couple more times in the following months until, one day, communication ceased between us. It felt so sudden and abrupt, considering how well we'd been getting along. *Was it something I said?* I attempted to make contact with him, but nothing. He'd 'ghosted' me. Not that 'ghosting' was a well-known thing back in the days of the Nokia 3310. There must have been a gap in his curriculum too, as he was nowhere to be seen at the college. Or had something terrible happened? My young, insecure self assumed it was something in me that had caused him to flee.

Twelve months would pass before we encountered one another again. It was a night of celebration. I was with a group of friends having a few drinks for my birthday, and we decided to head to the local nightclub to dance and party. I love to dance and have been labelled on more than one occasion as the 'best daggy dancer ever'. A badge I wear with great honour!

I was dancing with my back to the entrance, when my friend from college said through gritted teeth. "You won't believe this, but Trent is here, and he's coming over." We had one of those awkward conversations you have when you don't want others to know you're talking about them—her teeth gritted as she spoke to me through them, me standing as still as a statue. I felt a tap on my shoulder, turned around and there in front of me stood Trent. Despite having gone AWOL for almost a year, I found him as handsome as the first day I'd seen him. The initial conversation didn't last long. He wished me happy birthday, and then we each went back to our circle of friends. I remember asking him at the time how he knew it was my birthday, and apparently, he remembered from our conversations a year prior. I was somewhat impressed but proceeded with caution. Later that evening, we encountered each other again and ended up talking for nearly four hours on one of the couches outside the entrance to the nightclub. I am fairly certain those couches are either for making out or passing out, but that night we found them to be the perfect place for a conversation. I'm not sure why I felt like giving him the time of day, considering how abruptly he'd disappeared from my life a year earlier, but I saw something genuine in him. There was a warmth and a softness in his presence that I found comforting.

In the early hours of the morning, I drove Trent home. He attempted to kiss me goodbye, but I did the ultimate burn, turning my face to the side with his lips pressing against my cheek. I was determined to play it cool and approach him with caution, for I didn't wish to be left in the dark again.

Trent and I saw more and more of each other from week to week and began to develop strong feelings towards one another. He explained to me he'd stopped speaking to me before because of our age difference. Though we had a strong connection and got along well, he was seven years my senior. "Things were different now," he said. We both agreed it could have been handled differently and chose to move on.

Towards the end of that year, we decided to be together in an 'official' relationship, with our connection only growing stronger as the days and weeks went on. That coming December would prove our first challenge, as I had arranged a solo trip to Ireland to see my brother and his now-wife. Trent and I would be physically separated for a few weeks, which doesn't really sound like much now, but being fresh in love we wanted to spend every waking moment together.

Throughout my time overseas, Trent regularly visited my parents' place to hang out and have dinner with them. This appeared to me to be a genuine display of maturity and commitment. When I arrived back on Australian soil, he was there to meet me at the airport and organised a weekend away at the Gold Coast. We had a beautiful time, battling nerves and sharing our deep feelings for one another.

Our relationship deepened from there, and we experienced a lot of love and joy together. We'd often go away camping over the weekends and would always be outdoors fishing or exploring nature. After a couple of years of being together and saving all our money, we made the decision to purchase our first home in Brisbane, minutes from my parents' place. I remember the lead-up to buying the house. Trent and I would often go for drives or call the other to tell them about a cute little house that we'd seen and felt would be 'perfect'. Trent phoned me one day to tell me about this lovely little place around the corner from where my mum and dad lived. It was an adorable single-storey home on a big block of land. The only problem was the house wasn't for sale. Still, we mused over how perfect something like that would be for the two of us, picturing ourselves in it, dreaming about renovating and making it our own.

I can't remember how much time passed between that first conversation about the house and our next, but it was quick— maybe as little as a week. Trent was on his way home from work when he called. "Guess what, darlin'. You know that little house around the corner from your mum and dad's? Well, it's for sale!"

We worked hard and went to multiple banks and borrowers to see if we could get a loan for the property. At the time, the house was for sale for $350,000, which was more than we could afford to borrow, so we made an offer of around $330,000. They were quick to knock us back, and we were both pretty deflated at the setback, but determined to keep saving towards our dream. By this time, I was working as a massage therapist in a day spa and not earning a great income, so I decided to use my office administration skills and head back into the corporate world to increase my income and help our savings along.

Over the next six months, we became excited first-home-owners-in-the-making, saving every dollar we could and filling the spare room of my parents' place with household items like cutlery, linen and all the bits and pieces we would need when we eventually bought a home. Back in the day, people used to refer to such items gathered together as a 'glory box'. In our world, it became a 'glory room'.

When we were ready to try again for a home loan, we had everything we needed in terms of 'stuff' to fill the place, and a very impressive deposit. Now, all we needed was the perfect little home. And if you can believe it, almost six months later, the home we had fallen in love with all those months earlier was still for sale! We went through the process and made an offer (which was pretty much the same amount they'd laughed at a year earlier), and the place was ours.

Prior to moving in, we took the time to rip up all the old maroon carpet to expose the beautiful polished timber floors beneath and give the place a fresh coat of paint. We even went as far as building a white picket fence out the front. I look back on this now and smile. We built a seemingly perfect life together. A life people dream of having. White picket fence and all.

We both loved the house and spent most of our spare time, energy and hard-earned cash renovating and making it beautiful. It was our own little beach shack and sanctuary. It was close to the bay for our weekend fishing adventures, and it was really helpful at times to have my parents nearby, especially on Sundays when Mum would cook a roast dinner.

In 2009, Trent went away with a bunch of his fisherman friends to a place further north in Queensland. This was a bi-annual boys' trip that involved months of planning over many beers and gatherings. At the time, I remember feeling like I would really miss him. We were spending every waking moment together, going on epic adventures, making our new house feel like a home, and creating lots of beautiful memories. The thought of time apart brought about a sense of sadness. For some reason, it felt more difficult to see him go away for those few weeks than it ever had before. While he was away, we communicated as often as we could via satellite phone, and I enjoyed hearing the stories of all the big fish, sharks and whales they'd seen.

Not long after he'd returned from the trip, Trent offered to take me away for one night to Stradbroke Island—a beautiful piece of paradise and a short ferry ride from our home. It's one of those places in Australia where you can drive on the beach, so we'd often take our old ute over and camp for the weekend on the Island. He'd spent some time on the Island growing up and still had family who lived there. I remember him being so persistent in wanting to take me there for one night. The logical part of me argued with him that it would be better to wait until the following week so we could spend the whole weekend together at the beach rather than carting everything over for just one night. This seemed like a rational approach to me. Little did I know, Trent had a plan for us that particular weekend and he couldn't wait to share it with me. Since going away for one night wasn't the best idea, we agreed to wait for another time to go to Stradbroke. Instead, we got fish and chips and headed down to the local boat ramp with our two dogs. It was there that Trent asked me to marry him. I said yes.

Fast forward a few years, and we were married on a property

tucked away in the hills of Northern NSW. Before choosing the date and location, we'd talked about three other places for the wedding and moved the dates around a number of times, always prioritising something else until finally deciding to go ahead and make it happen.

Looking back to the lead-up to our marriage, 1 can see many signals indicating that perhaps this shouldn't have been the path 1 took with Trent. While we had a beautiful and loving relationship, it wasn't without its challenges. Many of our personal values were aligned, but some were not, and this caused tension in our relationship. Neither of us was particularly comfortable with conflict and often chose to avoid having conversations about our differences. But bottling up and suppressing our emotions wasn't healthy, eventually they began to spill over.

Still, our wedding was one of the best I've been to, even now. It was a simple outdoor ceremony under a beautiful old tree. We hung jars of wildflowers from its branches and set out bales of hay for the guests to sit on. In our conversations with the celebrant leading up to the wedding day, we shared our desire for a simple wedding ceremony. 1 wasn't keen on anything that dragged on too long, instead, hoping for something short and sweet. 1 even gave her a time limit—not wanting it to go on for longer than ten minutes!

It was my desire for the day to be as non-wedding-like as possible. No formalities. No speeches. No bridesmaids. No groomsmen. 1 don't know if 1 ever really wanted to be married in the traditional sense. There are those people in life who spend their early years dreaming about how their wedding day will be. Collecting images and items for when their time comes. Young women, who fantasise about the dress they will wear, and the place they will marry. 1 am certainly not one of those people. Other than thinking that 1 probably should, 1 don't know that 1 ever felt a deep desire within me to marry another person. I knew in my heart what I felt for Trent was real, and what we had together was beautiful, yet there was something else inside of me whispering. I can't explain it in words, and I couldn't at the time, other than to say there was a deeper knowing in my heart that perhaps this marriage wasn't for me.

Following on from the ceremony, we held a reception at a local property. Our friends brought their tents and camper trailers and stayed overnight. The food was homely, made by a local cook, and we had a selection of cakes on offer for the guests to enjoy. I spent the whole night on the barnyard dance floor, barely speaking to anyone until the roast pork rolls arrived at midnight. The vibe was definitely festival-like, a relaxed party to which I just happened to arrive in a formal wedding gown.

A couple of weeks later, we set off on our honeymoon to Thailand, where we enjoyed two beautiful weeks of amazing sunshine, the ocean, and beautiful food on the coast. It was only after returning home, and having been married for a little while, that our conversations turned towards family and starting one of our own. I didn't have a burning desire to become a mother any more than I wanted to marry. Some women know from very early on in their lives that they are destined for motherhood. They would hold a child with such grace and ease. They seemingly knew what to do, without really knowing at all. Their eyes would shine with a softness so pure and love-filled as they'd look into the child's eyes. They seemed content. The children they hold are content. That definitely wasn't me. If someone handed me a baby, it was wet with my sweat within five minutes. How I was holding them, felt awkward, not only to me, but also to them. Almost always, the baby would end up in tears. I didn't know what to do or how to do it. I hadn't spent a lot of time with mothers and babies to observe how it's done. I didn't feel that I knew the way. Yet, despite all of this awkwardness, I knew I could be loving and gentle. After all, we had a pet dog who I adored and treated with so much love. Based on my track record with other kids, I didn't know if I could love a small human as much as I loved this dog, but I was willing to explore this new territory with Trent and find out.

When we decided it would be a good time to 'start trying', I assumed it would probably take some time before I actually fell pregnant so I could prepare for what was to come. But to my great surprise, I fell pregnant the first time around—confirmed at home on one of those pee-on-the-stick tests. I would joke with others about how Trent only had to walk past me, and I fell pregnant. We were one of the lucky couples who immediately became pregnant with very little effort. I felt shocked at the swiftness in my falling, and I felt the nervous energy swirling around inside of me and the questions beginning to ask themselves. *Am I really ready for this? What if I am a shit mother? What if I don't enjoy being a mother? What if I don't like the baby? What if it doesn't like me? The house isn't finished. What if it isn't finished in time for the birth?*

All answers would be revealed in the months that followed.

Two

Falling

Doubt shifted to awe during the first trimester as I began to notice the first changes in my body. I was amazed by its ability to create, nurture and house another human. The feelings of panic and doubt I'd felt about the kind of mother I would be were replaced with a sense of calm. I was grateful to be pregnant in a world where many struggled to be. And together, we looked forward with great anticipation to our lives changing forever when our baby arrived.

The first trimester was physically and emotionally challenging. I experienced morning sickness daily, which wasn't just in the morning. This was another surprise to me, having known nothing about pregnancy previously. I was hypersensitive and cried about almost anything. One night, we were eating dinner together. Throughout my meal, all I could think about was the small container of butter chicken in the fridge left over from the night before. I couldn't wait to finish my meal and devour the butter chicken. I am quite fond of butter chicken! I turned to Trent and said, "Maybe I'll have the leftover curry from last night now." I was ravenous. I wanted that butter chicken! This was going to be great. Only Trent's face gave away his nervousness that all was not well with the butter chicken situation. He looked guilty. And was that distress I detected? "Ah babe, I already ate it..." And with that, I broke down and bawled my eyes out. I cried because there was no curry in the fridge. Hello hormones!

Despite the sickness and rollercoaster of emotion, the first trimester was fairly straightforward. We shared the news of our pregnancy with the majority of our family and friends prior to our thirteen-week scan. Keeping secrets from our friends and family isn't really how we rolled. We were very aware of the rate of miscarriage being high, and we thought if something were to happen to the baby, we would have a wonderful support network around us to help us through.

Our thirteen-week scan is a wonderful memory. My mum came along with us, and it was so cool to see the baby for the first time up close and to hear its little heart beating. I was in awe of this tiny human growing inside me, and of my body's innate ability to do it all without needing my assistance or intervention.

The scan showed that our baby was happy and healthy, and we were free to share the news with the masses. So, we did. At the time, neither of us had a social media account, nor did we feel called to participate in any of the pregnancy reveals that have become increasingly popular today. Instead, we reached out to people by phone or sent text messages to share the great news.

I was so calm and content as I moved into the second trimester. The little things didn't seem to bother me as much as they used to. The sickness had ceased. I enjoyed 'normal' food again. I felt amazing. I would stand in the bathroom each week and take photos of my body. I loved watching my body grow and expand. I felt radiant and beautiful.

During the second trimester, I felt the baby move for the very first time. I was lying on our bed before work one morning, hands on my stomach, headphones in my ears as I listened to Xavier Rudd's cover of the Bob Marley classic 'No Woman No Cry'. And then BAM! The kick-in-the-guts I'd been waiting for. *Great taste in music, kid.* Sensing the baby move for the first time was reassuring, yet strange at the same time as I felt another life growing inside me.

The time came for our twenty-week scan. We opted for a cheaper alternative this time around, a local place right next door to the hospital. Our appointment was first up in the morning, and we were due to see our obstetrician straight afterwards for a regular check-up and to talk through anything that may have come up in the scan. I remember being amazed at how much the baby had grown since the thirteen-week scan. I was fascinated by the black and white pictures on the screen in front of me. We had the option of finding out the sex of the baby but chose to keep it as a surprise.

Amid the excitement, I was uneasy as I replayed a conversation I'd had at the dentist a few weeks earlier. At the end of my appointment, after having a tooth repaired, I was speaking with the receptionist about all thing's pregnancy-related, when all of a sudden, she shared something deeply moving with me. She told me of the heartache she'd felt only a few years prior when her baby had died. At twenty weeks gestation, her baby died in utero. He had been stillborn. As I stood there listening, nineteen and a half weeks pregnant, she explained in detail the unimaginable pain of labouring and then birthing a baby that wasn't alive. Tears filled her eyes as she recalled the memory, and I began to ruminate on why she felt the need to tell me such a thing, knowing I was almost twenty weeks pregnant with my first child. *Was this something I needed to worry about? Was this common? Is my baby okay? Will my baby be okay?*

As I lay awaiting my twenty-week scan a few days later, the same questions resurfaced. It was a long appointment with lots of checking and measuring—more than I remembered from the first scan. Towards the end, the woman told us she had seen something in the placenta that concerned her, and she wanted a second opinion from her supervisor. I wondered what she'd seen. She wandered off out of the room, returning moments later with another woman. They were standing together at the machine, talking in what felt like their own secret language. I found it challenging to stay calm through it all. They tried to explain to us what they were seeing, but we didn't understand. No matter how many different ways they put it, it made little sense. I was becoming increasingly agitated, so I suggested our obstetrician, who we were seeing straight after, could help us understand if they sent him the report.

As we sat down in the obstetrician's office a short time later, I explained what had just happened. He asked me for the scans and looked over them straight away. "Ah, this is what they are referring to. You see those there? They're called lakes. They're common in pregnancy, and lots of women go on to have happy and healthy babies. You don't need to be concerned about them at all."

Relief. Our baby was going to be okay.

From that moment on, things felt different. I felt different. Something shifted within me. Though I still felt calm, an underlying sense of worry began to build. I replayed the conversations with the sonographer and the obstetrician over and over in my head.

Was everything okay with our baby? Are lakes really normal in a placenta? What does this all mean?

A couple of weeks later, I spent the day down at Brunswick Heads with my parents. It was a hot summer's day. The water was crystal clear. The sun shone brightly in an uninterrupted blue sky. I sat on the beach, looking down at my beautiful belly in my swimmers. Despite the gorgeous weather, I remember feeling a little off. I was reserved and hadn't felt the baby move much throughout the day. I remember Mum asking me if I was okay, as I was not my normal chirpy self. Intuitively, something didn't feel right. When I returned home that evening, I sent a text message to our obstetrician explaining how I was feeling and that I hadn't felt the baby move much throughout the day. He called me within half an hour and asked me to go in and see him.

I took a friend with me as Trent was out west visiting my brother. When we arrived, the obstetrician took us straight into his office and turned the scanner on. He moved it all around until he located the heart. The heartbeat was strong. The baby was bouncing around, making up its own dance moves and showing off for the audience! Everything was okay. Our baby was okay. I was okay. "Welcome to parenthood," the doctor said. "A place where you constantly worry about the health and wellbeing of your children—no matter how old they are." We had a giggle.

I was due to see the doctor again in five days for my regular monthly check-up. I was excited for the appointment as I couldn't wait for Trent to see how much the baby had grown since our twenty-week scan. I was also excited as my sister-in-law Emily was coming along to meet the obstetrician and, of course, her soon-to-be niece or nephew. My sister-in-law was also my birthing partner. I thought I'd better have someone other than Trent with me in the birthing suite; he often felt giddy at the sight of blood. I'd more than likely need some reinforcements on the day of birthing.

Friday, 21 February 2014 is a day forever etched in my memory. Emily and I made our way to the appointment. I'd received a call earlier that morning from Trent in a huff to say that he'd been held up for a job and may not make it to the appointment in time. I felt disappointed, though I knew there'd be other opportunities for him to see the progress.

I laid down on the bed, rolled up my shirt and turned my head towards the screen. I remember the doctor saying, 'It's about time you popped'. A phrase often used to describe the moment when a woman all of a sudden looks pregnant. Then there was a knock at the door. It was Trent. He'd managed to make it, after all. It had been a big couple of weeks I felt mounting up from the conversation at the dentist, the slight complication at the twenty-week scan and the absence of me feeling the baby move. So, when he walked through the door, I was relieved to see him.

"Oh, look at that. He's looking at you," the doctor said, as we saw the face of the baby on the screen. He rolled the scanner around some more until it was over the heart. I was familiar with what things were now as I had been to quite a few scans. I could make out the bones and other parts of the body. The baby no longer resembled a black and white blur on a screen. I could see all four chambers of the heart very clearly on the screen. And then it struck me. Something was missing. A wave of emotion began to swell inside of me as I realised what it was. There was no flicker. Nothing ticking inside. There was no heartbeat. I looked up at the doctor, whose facial expression was one of concern. He was silent as he stepped away from the machine.

"Jacqui, when was the last time you felt this baby move?"

My heart sank. My eyes filled, ready to burst. "There's no heartbeat, is there?"

The doctor bowed his head, unable to get the words out, instead, looking into my eyes, his also full of tears. Slowly, he shook his head.

I sat up and cupped my head in my hands. I wept and wailed, instantly struck by overwhelming heartache. Trent paced around the room, shocked and devastated by what he'd just heard. Emily sat in a chair in the corner of the room, holding in tears of her own. What a moment for us all. None of us saw this coming. I'd seen the baby five days ago, and the heartbeat was strong. Now it was gone. What happened?

A few moments passed before anyone spoke. The doctor went first. "I want you to walk right out of here this afternoon and do nothing but be together. Come to terms with what you've heard this afternoon. I will see you on Monday morning to begin the 'process'. Nothing will happen to you over the weekend. I will contact you on Sunday, but for now, just be together."

We did as he said, getting up and walking straight out of there. As we left, we passed a heavily pregnant woman in the reception area. I walked as fast as I could with my head down until I reached the car park. It was here I found a place to rest on the concrete gutter in the heat of the full summer's sun. I sat here for what felt like an hour, and I sobbed uncontrollably. I don't even remember what Trent was doing. Emily was a godsend, not only providing comfort and support to us in those initial moments following on from discovering our baby had died, but also beginning the process of notifying our family. I am so grateful she was there with us that day.

Trent's brother organised some accommodation for us at the Gold Coast for the weekend. Before we left, I wanted to go back inside and talk to the doctor about what came next. I craved some kind of certainty. I didn't want to go away for the weekend without knowing what we would be walking back into on Monday morning. The doctor saw us straight away.

"How do we get the baby out?" I asked.

"You will birth the baby, like you would in a normal labour," he replied.

"Will I have contractions and experience all the same kinds of sensations?"

"Yes, you will."

"Is there any other way?"

"You can request a caesarean birth, though I wouldn't recommend this, as your physical recovery will be a lot longer, on top of everything else. We will give you a drug. It will be inserted into your vagina every six hours. It will dissolve and cause a chemical reaction in your body, telling it to go into labour. Then you will birth the baby and the placenta as you would if your baby was alive."

The doctor once again reassured me that I would be safe and taken care of and encouraged me to go be with Trent for the weekend and have time to grieve the loss of our baby.

We checked into the apartment and went straight up to the room, turned our phones to silent and focused our attention on one another and what was ahead of us. We had many conversations over those two days. We spoke at length about the process we were about to experience—labour, birth, death, grief, joy, sadness. We had so many unanswered questions. *What sex was the baby? What name would we choose? What would the baby look like? Would we hold the baby? Would we get any answers as to what caused our baby to die?*

Personally, I struggled most with the thought of having to give birth to a baby that was no longer alive. As the weekend went on, I would find myself looking down at my full stomach, and I would sob with a heavy heart, trying to comprehend the incomprehensible— giving birth to death.

I chose only to wear loose-fitting clothes over the weekend as the thought of someone asking me how far along I was, or when I was due, was far too overwhelming. I remember thinking ... *What would I tell them, you know, if someone asked me when I was due? Would I tell them the baby wasn't alive? That I was just carrying it around inside of me for a few days before I could get into the hospital to birth it.* It seemed a whole lot easier to hide it all from the world.

I spent a lot of time on the balcony staring out at the ocean and writing in my journal. Trying my best to get a handle on the situation. Trying to come to some kind of acceptance of what was and preparing my body and my mind for the mammoth task ahead. It felt impossible. We returned home on Sunday afternoon and put together a text message to send out to our extended friends and family. We decided to let everyone know our baby had died, as we knew their love and support would help us in the coming days. I also felt this was a way of removing the awkwardness in telling people about what had happened if I were to run into them in the street. They responded with an outpouring of love and kindness. We kept every single text message, and I read them over and over as I waited in the hospital bed, preparing to give birth. They gave me strength, encouragement and a deeper knowing that we were all loved and cared for.

I began the process of birthing my baby at 6:00am on Monday, 24 February 2014. We arrived early at the hospital and made our way to the front desk. The lady looked up at me and asked for the details of my admission, as well as my healthcare card. I was unable to speak. Tears streamed down my face as I gestured to Trent to talk to the woman and to do all of the administrative tasks she was requesting.

After checking in, we were given further details on what to do next. Walking towards the reception area, I noticed it was eerily quiet for a hospital ward. I looked around at the beautiful artworks covering the walls, a vase of pink lilies resting perfectly on the front desk. That's when I saw her. Our eyes met and softened as we approached one another. Our obstetrician Owen had sent us a message the night before explaining what would happen, so we had some certainty about what to expect when we got there. Upon our arrival, we were to ask for his midwife Elizabeth, who would be taking care of us during our stay. "Jacqui?" she said. I nodded as I began to weep once more, overcome with emotion at the extraordinary challenge ahead of us. We reached our arms out to one another, and in the warmth of her embrace, I knew everything was going to be okay. Elizabeth led us to the private room where we would be staying. I felt such relief when we learned we would be separated from the hospital's main maternity ward, instead, placed in a section of the hospital where people recovered from surgery. I cannot imagine how much harder things would have been if we were thrown in among other birthing mothers with living babies at what was already such a difficult time.

The first thing Elizabeth showed us were some butterflies on our door. She explained these were a message system to the hospital staff. It helped them understand that behind the door was a family grieving and dealing with a stillbirth. Those thoughtful little touches made our stay and our stillbirth experience a little more manageable.

Owen arrived not long after and sat with us prior to Elizabeth administering the first lot of tablets. He gave us some more information in terms of the length of time it would take from the first lot of tablets being inserted to the birth of the baby. "The quickest I have seen it happen from start to finish is ten hours, the longest is three days. I would advise you to be prepared to stay here for a minimum of three days." This caught me off guard. *Three days? Really? It could take that long?* I don't know how long I had expected it to take, but three days seemed like an excessive amount of time. I'm not sure if it was my way of coping, but I remember saying to him that I was going to set a new record by being quicker than the ten hours. We all had a laugh.

The first tablets were inserted on Monday morning. It was uncomfortable, but not painful at all. We spent the day in the hospital room, reading, relaxing, and joking. Although I started the day off very emotional, I became surprisingly upbeat as time went on. I'm unsure as to why this is—perhaps a coping mechanism or some kind of self-protection. Either way, there was a nice energy in the room, and the vibes were fairly high considering what we were going through.

Elizabeth handed me a beautiful box covered in orange flowers and butterflies. Its contents were a number of resources for families experiencing stillbirth. It contained things like a journal, pen, crochet beanie and booties, a photo frame with a butterfly and a beautifully bound book with a number of heartfelt stories written by families who had stillborn babies. I took the time to read every page. I found great comfort in these stories. The pages were full of stories of love, loss, grief, fear, hope, joy and every other emotion imaginable. The parts of the stories that resonated most with me were those where the families spoke of their regrets. 'I regretted not holding my baby.' 'We didn't give her a name until many years later.' 'We didn't have any photos with him.' And so on. I made a promise to myself as I sat up in the bed that I wouldn't live with any regrets following this experience. I would do everything these families said they regretted not doing. Even if they felt excruciating, I would do them.

There were no physical changes as the hours passed, and as the end of the day grew near, I became disheartened realising I would not be birthing my baby on this day.

When I woke the following day, Tuesday, 25 February, my mood had certainly shifted. I felt like going inward. I was mellow and subdued. The upbeat energy I'd felt the day before had left my body as the realisation that I'd be birthing my baby any time from now began to set in. I felt agitated from being in the hospital room the previous day. I wanted to get out and breathe in the fresh air and feel the warmth of the sun on my skin. I've always found nature to be one of the greatest healers in my life.

We sat down at the café across the road for a snack and something to drink. It was so good to be out in the fresh air, and I instantly felt my mood shifting and my body relaxing with each breath. As we made our way back to the hospital at about 10:30am, I felt something happening in my body. "Emily! I think I am having a contraction." Followed by, "Yep, definitely something happening."

We went back up to our room and met with Elizabeth and explained what was happening. Elizabeth reassured me this was a positive step forward in the process and that things were certainly starting to progress. I spent some time bouncing up and down on a fitball, breathing through each surge, as well as going for short walks through the corridors. There was a moment when I was bouncing away that Elizabeth offered me some pain relief—a shot of pethidine in the leg. At first, I declined, saying the pain was manageable and that I could do it without the pain relief. Elizabeth replied, "I know you can probably go on without any pain relief, but why would you put yourself through more physical pain than you need to? This is already an extremely painful situation. Let us help you." And with that, I accepted her offer. The shot of pethidine certainly provided some immediate pain relief, and I felt a sense of relaxation come over me.

There came a moment that afternoon when the reality of what I was about to do hit me. I was sitting in the shared common room with Emily and Elizabeth when a wave of emotion washed over me, and I began to cry. "I don't know how to do this. How do I give birth to a baby I know isn't alive? I just can't. It's too much to bear. I don't know how to do this." And that really was the truth of how I felt at that moment. The concept of birthing death was far too great for my mind to comprehend. I remember Elizabeth comforting me, looking me in the eyes and saying, "You can, and you will." And I cried and cried and cried some more.

As the afternoon went on, I became increasingly anxious at the thought of Elizabeth not being there for the birth of our baby. We'd formed a strong connection over the previous twenty-four hours, and I felt a sense of safety and comfort in her presence. By this time in the day, Elizabeth had worked two back-to-back shifts and was due for a rest break as per the hospital's policy. Elizabeth was due to leave at 4:00pm that afternoon. The thought of having some random come in at the last moment, after having formed such a strong bond with Elizabeth, felt like another cut to an already deeply wounded woman.

In the lead-up to her finish time, Elizabeth introduced us to a midwife named Jo, who would be supporting us through the afternoon and into the evening. I was nervous. *What if I didn't vibe with her? What if she wasn't warm and nurturing?* All these questions swam around in my mind as I anxiously awaited our meeting. I exhaled a sense of relief when I met Jo. She was warm and kind and showed genuine care and interest in me and us. Once again, I knew everything would be okay.

Three

Jack

At 3:55pm, while laying down and having a rest, my waters broke. A steady flow of warm liquid gushed from my body. It was very unlike the scenes you see in the movies when a woman's water breaks. This was messy with lots and lots of blood mixed in. Despite the mess, it felt magical and beautiful. I was at peace in that moment, and it is one that is etched in my memory and my heart.

As soon as I announced my water had broken, Trent leapt to his feet, and I swear he sprinted out of the room so fast, even Usain Bolt would've had a hard time keeping up with him. He found Elizabeth. She was still there and came rushing into the room with Jo. Soon after, Owen entered the room, panting and short of breath after having sprinted over from his office to be with us.

As we all prepared for the birth of the baby, Elizabeth and Jo were talking about moving me, so they'd be able to put fresh sheets on the bed. When they asked if they could change the bed linen to make it more comfortable, I was very quick to decline the offer. I lay there in what others might perceive as a 'mess' but to me, it was beautiful. For the past six months, this warm liquid had surrounded our baby, providing a layer of cushioning and protection as it grew in my womb. It was something I didn't want to be free from. I found comfort in its warmth.

The room was darkened with the lights dimmed down so low it felt cave-like. There were six of us in the room, yet all I could hear was the clock ticking. No one made a sound or felt the need to fill the silence, which made the birthing process and my experience all the more beautiful. I was very aware of the sensations in my body. I felt no urge to push, with my body doing all the work on its own. I knew in every moment what was happening purely by feeling it all. *Okay, that's the feet out.* Another wave would come. *Okay, that's the lower body out.* At this point, I asked about the gender. "It's a little … boy." I exclaimed to Trent, "I fucking told you!" We all shared a moment of laughter. Then came the head. The surges intensified. *I think I need gas. Yep, I'm going to ask for some gas. This is a really intense feeling.* And then it would subside. And then it would return. And so on and so forth. I found I could always calm myself and breathe through the discomfort rather than opting for gas to help, which is something I look back on and feel very proud of.

At 4:35pm on 25 February 2014, after a relatively quick labour, I gave birth to a beautiful baby boy we named Jack. He was 410 grams and 30cm long. His eyes were closed. He looked as though he were in a deep and peaceful sleep.

In the moments after giving birth, Jo asked me if I'd like to hold Jack. I said no. I didn't feel ready to embrace him at that point. I knew I would, but in those initial moments following his birth, I just wasn't ready. Perhaps I could sense something else was coming. Even though Jack wasn't alive at the time of his birth, he was treated and cared for as if he was. When I turned to look at Jo, she'd wrapped him in a beautiful baby blanket and was nursing him, talking to him as if he could hear her, as if he were alive. I will never forget the beauty in that image. I am still moved to tears when I recall it. What an incredible woman. A woman who can embrace death with such grace and love.

Physically things weren't finished for me. I still needed to birth the placenta. Owen and Elizabeth had informed me that I would have some contractions about twenty minutes after birthing Jack and to let them know when I felt those coming on, as this would be the indication the placenta was ready to be birthed. When the sensations started, I alerted them. The placenta wasn't quite ready to come away as it naturally would at full-term, so Owen grabbed hold of the umbilical cord and Elizabeth massaged my stomach pretty firmly to help it. With all the pulling and pushing, the cord snapped, and Owen flung back in his chair (no joke.) We had to find another way to help it along. "Let's try an age-old trick." Owen handed me a bedpan and asked me to sit on the toilet. He explained that sometimes the act of sitting down encourages the body to expel and release. We hoped this would be the case for the placenta.

As soon as I sat down, I blacked out. I'd lost a fair amount of blood through the combination of my waters breaking and birthing Jack, and my body was becoming weak. When I came to, I was still on the toilet but was being stripped down to my underwear and being dressed in a gown to be taken into the theatre for emergency surgery.

Fear took over my whole body as I was wheeled out of the room, down the hallway, and into the theatre preparation area. I'd gone from this peaceful, tranquil, cave-like birthing room to a bright, sterile and very hectic environment. The theatre nurse threw all the paperwork on top of my legs and rushed to fill things out and stick stickers here, there and everywhere—she did this on top of me. The pace at which everyone moved around me was fast. I'm not sure if it was the shock and trauma of what I'd been through, but I honestly thought in that moment I was going to die, so much so that I remember turning to Owen and asking him with tears streaming down my face if I was. He took my hand and said, "No, you will not die, and you don't need to worry. Keep looking at me, and don't worry until I look worried." Needless to say, he never looked the slightest bit concerned.

I said goodbye to Trent and was wheeled into the operating theatre, where Owen would surgically remove the placenta. Owen introduced me to the anaesthetist, Chris, who explained the next steps and placed the mask over my nose and mouth. I inhaled a couple of slow, deep breaths before drifting off. And then I was awake again after what felt like only a few minutes. The first thing I heard when I opened my eyes was a woman's voice saying: "Graham, Graham. Can you hear me, Graham? GRAHAM!" *Oh no ... fuck me, Graham has carked it*. I never found out what happened to Graham. Hopefully, he came around. Owen was there too. How special for a doctor to be so supportive in such a traumatic time in one's life. I'll always remember those moments.

Owen wheeled me back up to the room where I'd given birth and the first thing I saw was Trent nursing baby Jack. I was completely overcome with emotion. In the days leading up to the birth, we'd had many conversations about how we thought we might cope with certain things like holding the baby. Trent had shared that he probably wouldn't want to, as he wouldn't feel comfortable. For this to be the first thing I saw when entering the room, my heart cracked open a little.

After some time, Jack was taken to the hospital's internal morgue to ensure his body was kept cool. The midwives reassured us that any time we wanted to see him, all we needed to do was ask, and he would be brought to us.

It wasn't until the following day that I felt ready to hold Jack. I'd had a rough night and was still feeling extremely weak from the combination of the physical and emotional trauma. My body was so weak that a midwife bathed me in the bed with wipes and helped me when I needed to go to the toilet. I felt raw and very exposed— totally dependent on another to help me with the things I'd always been capable of doing on my own. This was something I had to surrender to. Another thing I wasn't prepared for. After my wash, I expressed to the midwife Amanda that I was ready to see baby Jack, and that I wanted to hold him.

She went away, and when she returned, he was dressed in some tiny clothes and wrapped in a blanket. Amanda gestured to me. I reached out with open arms and cradled Jack in my hands. He still looked as though he were in a deep sleep, only I knew he wouldn't be waking from this one. Tears flowed as I thought about all the expectations previously placed on us. He was the first grandchild on my side of the family. He was our first child. We thought we would be raising a child in a few months. We'd prepared for parenthood. We'd prepared for a baby to enter our lives. I felt sad for my parents as I felt I'd let them down. I felt sad for Trent as I felt I'd let him down. And I felt sad for Jack as I felt that I had failed as a mother, unable to sustain him and see him through until the end.

As the day went on, my body was struggling to regain its strength. With every attempt to stand on my own two feet and walk to the bathroom, I'd collapse. One of the midwives gave me a bed pan so I wouldn't have to stand. She also brought warm washers and bathed me in bed. Although this level of care was exceptional, it was a challenge for me to surrender to it all and completely depend on others to help me with basic things like washing and going to the toilet.

By the time the afternoon came, there was talk of a blood transfusion being ordered for the evening. Owen came to me and explained the transfusion process. In his opinion, this was the most suitable option for me, considering my physical state. I agreed to have the transfusion, albeit shaking in my bed with intense uncertainty about what the experience would be like. All I knew for sure were the bare facts. Three bags of blood given to me via a drip through the night, in hopes they would be enough to replenish my supply and give me the physical strength I needed to go on.

By the time the first bag of blood was hooked up, I was incredibly anxious. I didn't know what to expect in terms of how it would feel and how my body would respond to foreign blood. I wanted to encourage my body to accept the process, to accept the blood, so I began an affirmation over and over: *I choose to accept this blood. I choose to accept this blood. I choose to accept this blood.*

Tracey was the midwife rostered on for the overnight shift. At first, she seemed a bit standoffish. I sensed there was something going on for her. It didn't take long for us to bond though, each of us sharing a tear as we talked about my experience. Tracey told me later in the night that she'd received an email from a friend in Hong Kong who was also a midwife, and also dealing with a family experiencing a stillbirth. She reminded me that it doesn't discriminate, and happens to women all over the world, from all walks of life. I felt sad again; for myself, her friend, and the grieving family across the globe in a similar situation.

The following morning, I had half expected to wake feeling like the incredible hulk—bulked and ready to smash after the blood transfusion. This wasn't to be. I was still very weak and struggled on my feet. It would be another day and a half before I had the strength to leave the hospital.

On the morning of our departure, we thanked the hospital staff for their love and support. I'd written letters to each of the midwives I felt a connection with, thanking them for their love, support and kindness, and I left those with the staff at the front reception desk. This experience was not only difficult for me, but for many of the people who were there supporting us. I wanted them to know how grateful I felt for their support.

Leaving the hospital without a baby in my arms was excruciating.

We'd just endured five days of the most intense experience of our lives—bringing a baby into the world. Instead of leaving with an eagerness to get our new baby home, we left in mourning, carrying only our heavy hearts with us. We walked from the ground-level foyer to the car park. I waited for Trent to bring the car around. As I stood there, I watched a new mother put her newborn baby into its brand-new car seat and I wept with a deep longing and sadness for my boy.

I was anxious to go home. I think because I knew this meant that my life would go on in some way ... although I didn't know how, or what that would look like. Trent had been travelling back and forth between home and the hospital over the week and had collected the numerous bunches of flowers and cards left on our doorstep and in our mailbox. It was nice to have the life of the flowers filling our space—the colours and the smells helping to shift my mood, even if only for a moment. I also noticed that our very bored and mischievous dog had dug out the corn from the veggie patch and ripped every single kernel off each of the cobs. The yellow kernels were like confetti littering our back lawn. It made me laugh.

Those first few weeks at home burst my heart open. I cried every single day for about three weeks straight. I felt like a part of me had died with baby Jack. A garden that once flourished within me was depleted of all life and quenching for water like the desert plains, longing for the rain.

Trent saw me in all of my vulnerability, and cared for me through those difficult hours, days and weeks immediately after Jack's birth. There were times when I didn't have the strength to move my body from the bed to the bathroom. Trent would come to me, help me to my feet and walk with me. He placed a chair in the shower, as even holding my body up to wash felt like an impossible task. He saw my weak, naked body, and he loved me anyway.

Jack's birth and death not only affected us as his parents, but many people in our immediate family. As their first grandchild, my parents had their own grieving to do for Jack. All of their hopes and expectations were gone in an instant. Instead of feeling joy for their daughter having birthed a baby, they were broken-hearted. When my mum visited me at the hospital, I didn't want her to cry in front of me. I went as far as asking my dad to tell her not to come if she was going to cry. Big emotional outpours were something we were not great at nurturing when I was growing up, and sometimes, I felt my tears were more of a burden than something natural and a way of healing. My mum and I had a pretty awkward relationship when I was young. We both struggled to show love to each other in ways we each recognised and valued. We didn't know any different. I could count on one hand the number of times we said we loved one another. We just weren't those types of people. We also didn't hug. Often embracing and patting the other on the back before quickly letting go. It makes me laugh now when I look back at how awkward we were, and at how far we have come.

When Jack was born, I felt the awkwardness between us began to change. We started spending more time together as a family and spoke on the phone more often. Over time, our relationship turned into something really beautiful. Don't get me wrong, we still tell each other where to go and what we think. We are from the burbs after all! But we can show love in ways we didn't know how to before. This was another one of the gifts Jack gifted to our family.

As part of our healing process, Trent drove us down to the water's edge most days, where together, we would watch the tide roll in and out. Sometimes we spoke. Other times we sat in silence—the silence only being broken by sniffles and tears as they streamed down our faces before falling into our laps. I don't know that we knew how to grieve for something so big, but just being there by the water and in each other's presence was all we needed in those early days to get through. I've always found such beauty and power in the ocean. It's vast and expansive, gentle and calm, ferocious and chaotic, all of which I felt within myself through my journey with grief. These trips continued in the weeks that followed, becoming a healing ritual for us, until it was time for Trent to return to work.

Four

Re-Birth

In the few weeks that followed Jack's death, the thought of Trent leaving the house without me sent me into an emotional spin where I became crippled with fear. My deepest fear was that something bad might happen to him too. As if the universe wasn't quite finished with me yet, and the thought of losing him as well was too much to bear. *How could I live on without my son and husband?* I didn't want to let him go, so I held on tightly. This holding on caused some tension between us. Trent felt the pressure from his work and the need for him to return. He also had me there, clinging on to him for dear life. I can only imagine how difficult it must have been. The day inevitably arrived when he went back to work. Alone with my thoughts, I was scared, holding so much grief inside, not knowing what to do with it, other than to cry it out.

As the days and weeks rolled on, I continued my routine of waking up, getting up, saying goodbye to Trent, and moving to the couch to cry. I had a steady stream of visitors in those first few weeks after Jack's death, and they helped me in many ways. They provided comfort to me in times of need; they brought me food and a shoulder to lean on, and they took the pressure off being on my own. I am grateful for every one of them. They also served as a bit of a distraction and a reprieve from having to feel the intense feelings inside of me. Some days, I just didn't want to deal with it. I longed to rest. I wanted to close myself off from it and to have a few moments of peace, to feel normal again and for my life to return to how it was before. I guess some might perceive this as being in denial or avoiding what had happened, but it was instinctual and necessary for me at the time.

With the busyness of life, it was inevitable there would come a time when people stopped checking in as regularly—after all, they had their own lives to live, their own families to care for. It was at this time, when I was once again on my own, that I began to cry. I was on the couch one morning after Trent had left for work, crying and feeling all the feelings of grief that had become the norm in my daily life. I would cry to complete exhaustion some days—my eyes swollen and dark, my body weak and heavy. Some days, I didn't get up off the floor. I'd sit there, curled up in the foetal position. I'd sob uncontrollably for hours on end. There were always more tears to cry. When I thought I couldn't possibly have any more in there, they'd flow once again. I wasn't eating well, if at all, and my mind was clouded by my own suffering. I was spiralling into a deep and dark place. It was a place I felt okay to visit, though I knew I couldn't stay there for long and allow it to consume me.

I needed to find another way to move through the immense grief I felt. I needed to move it through and out of my body to free it, and to free myself from its grasp. Through the tears, I said aloud on the couch ... "Jacqueline, you have a couple of choices here. You can either keep going down this path and spiral into a state of some kind of deep depression, locking yourself away and crying every single day, or you can choose to do something different. What is it going to be?" And with that question, I chose to do grief differently.

At first, I started off small—going out and buying some new activewear and a daily planner to inspire a sense of motivation within. I started by focusing my attention on the basics of feeling well physically and mentally. This included doing things like moving my body daily, eating good quality food, and listening to people who inspired me. I chose yoga to begin, moving my body gently and attended an over-fifties class at the local community centre where I was very clearly the youngest by many years. I went a couple of times and cried my eyes out; in fact, almost every yoga class I attended in the few years that followed Jack's death brought me to my knees and reduced me to tears. It was an invitation into stillness. It was a dedicated chunk of time set aside for me to see and feel all the things I needed to. My relationship with grief was challenging, but I always found the thing that helped me the most was to physically move my body. Yoga and dance became an outlet for my grief, as did writing. These may seem like seemingly insignificant choices, but made together, each and every day, they added up and helped me out of the depths of my own darkness.

Once I felt in flow and was consistently implementing these small changes every day, I moved on to some bigger ticket items, like looking at the people I was spending the most time with and deciding if they were positively influencing my life. This period of time was particularly challenging as I said goodbye to many friends who'd been in my life for some time. I distanced myself from others whose opinions and choices either didn't align with my own or caused me to judge myself or others.

Some of the people I was distancing myself from were friends we had spent a lot of time with previously. I noticed through this passage of time that we also began to drift apart. Trent couldn't understand why I didn't want to be around certain people anymore, as he wasn't going through the same transformation that I was. More space grew between us when he shared his desire for me to be the way I had been when we first were together, and for things to be the same. Yet I would never be that same woman again—how could I be? I was changing my mind about everything—what I valued, gaining clarity on what was and wasn't okay—and looking at the types of people I wanted to be around and places I wanted to be. I immersed myself in personal development, invested in my own learning, and surrounded myself with people who were walking their own paths to freedom. As I continued to walk my path, the distance between us grew. Deep down in our hearts, we feared the inevitable change that was coming.

In my bid for life to return to some kind of normality, I chose to return to my workplace only six weeks after giving birth. To say this was too soon is a complete understatement. I was not ready to be there, yet I placed so much unnecessary pressure on myself to get on with life and to move forward. As much as I judged Trent for him wanting me to be how I used to be, there was also a part of me that resisted changing. I feared letting go of things, or doing things differently, as I was uncertain what that would mean for my life going forward. So, I held on to certain things and forced myself back into situations without being fully prepared for them. On my first day back in the office, very uncharacteristically, I lashed out at a manager over the phone. I was so tired of his shit, of hearing him talk the corporate talk but lacking the backbone to follow through with his actions. My patience and tolerance for this kind of behaviour wore thin and I was unable to control the anger I felt inside. Perhaps my experience of death helped put life into perspective and revealed to me what did and didn't matter. The things I once placed so much emphasis and importance on— the corporate world, my job, people's opinions—no longer held any kind of power in my life. My outburst of anger resulted in the manager complaining to my boss about my behaviour. After a conversation with my boss, we both agreed I'd take some time off from dealing with clients until I felt more settled. This was a good option.

Returning to work also presented a number of awkward encounters with people who hadn't seen me for a while and did not understand what I had been through. There was no way I could've expected this before returning to work. My mind wasn't there. I often visited the cafeteria in the morning to get a coffee and would frequently bump into colleagues and friends. Being such a large organisation, the cafeteria was often a place to meet and socialise first thing and throughout the day. While waiting in line one morning, a friendly colleague approached me. His happy expression quickly turned to a look of what I can only describe as complete and utter confusion. The last time he had seen me was six weeks earlier, when I was unmistakably pregnant. He had no insight or understanding as to what had unfolded in my life since then. "Err ... Jacqui, you're back already. That was so quick." He awkwardly gazed at my stomach. I took a deep breath and closed my eyes for a few seconds before I spoke. I wasn't sure how to break it to him, other than to tell it how it was. My heart broke for this beautiful man as I prepared to share the truth of my situation with him. "Thank you. It's nice to see you. I'm sad to let you know that my baby passed away." Tears welled in his eyes as he told me how sorry he was for my loss. I could see he didn't know what to say or do in that moment. I felt for him. His sadness at the news seemed genuine, albeit not his own experience.

I had worked in the business for years and was well-known across many of the branches, having formed strong working relationships. The team I worked with did their best to reach as many people as possible and to communicate with them about my experience prior to my return to the office, but they couldn't get to everyone. Being a highly empathic human, I dreaded encounters with those people who didn't know. Not because I was afraid to talk about my experience. Not because I feared facing the truth.

I dreaded seeing the looks of sadness on their faces when I told them my baby hadn't survived. I felt for them in the moments they heard the words come out of my mouth, as I knew many of them wouldn't know what to say in reply. I was okay with not knowing what to say and do—I myself didn't know at times—but I felt that people sometimes needed to fill the silence with something. Other times, it was too much for them that they would abruptly end the conversation and high tail it out of there.

I remember a woman I worked with sitting with me one day and asking me how we could all get through it together, and what kinds of things would and wouldn't be helpful. I explained to her that I was comfortable sharing my experience. If people were curious as to the exact happenings—the ins and outs of it all—I would be happy to answer their questions. I also felt the deep desire to use Jack's name and I am very thankful they respected this request. Some people asked me about Jack. 'What did he look like?' 'What was it like birthing Jack?' I always felt safe to share my experience. I wanted to give voice to it as this felt like another layer of my healing.

It's not only the parents who grieve the loss of the child. There are so many other people who are affected by it, too. Friends and family also grieve in their own way and for their own reasons. It took me some time to work through all the guilt I felt and carried on behalf of my family and friends. I felt a sense of responsibility for the burden of grief I'd placed on them. I blamed and punished myself for a long time.

One of the hardest experiences for me to engage in after Jack was born was baby showers. I didn't have a baby shower, as I planned to have something closer to my due date. Several of our friends were at the stage where they were growing their families. Many pregnancies came and many babies were born in the few years that followed Jack's death. I felt courageous enough within myself to attend, to be there to celebrate with the expectant mother glowing in all of her pregnancy glory. Yet at the end, when the celebration was done, when we'd packed up, and I was on my way home, I almost always drove off in tears. I felt sad that I didn't get to that point of excitedly celebrating with my family and friends in anticipation of the baby's arrival. Perhaps it was yet another reminder of my circumstances and the uncertainty of what the future looked like for me as a mother. *Would I ever be fortunate enough to experience motherhood again? Was it written in the pages of my story? Or was this it for me?*

At home, we had a spare room full of baby clothes, a cot, a change table and all the baby things an expectant family gathers in anticipation of the arrival of their baby. I'd chosen to keep the door of the spare room closed for many weeks following Jack's death. I didn't feel ready to face what was in there. I couldn't bear the thought of pulling out all the beautiful clothes he would've been dressed in, of feeling the softness of the blankets he would've been wrapped up in. It was too much to deal with on top of every other feeling inside me. I kept the door closed until I felt strong enough to open it and see it all.

A couple of months later, I called my best friend who lived in Sydney at the time and asked her if she could come to Queensland to help me with the spare room. When I finally opened the door, I opened another door inside of me, revealing another layer of grief to be healed. Though I felt raw and exposed once again, I had an underlying sense of calm as we worked through all the things. It felt like progress. As we packed away all the baby clothes into vacuum bags, we couldn't help but notice they were mostly neutral and blue tones—appropriate for any gender, yet most likely for a boy. Whenever I bought something, my mum would say to me, 'Jacqueline, that's a bit boyish, don't you think?' Right throughout the pregnancy, in my heart, I knew I was having a boy, even without knowing in my head.

Once we'd packed everything up, I left the vacuum packs in the wardrobe for a while until I knew what to do with it all. In the months that followed, some of the items would be donated, while some would be given to pregnant women in my life who didn't feel weird about having them.

Trent and I were unsure if another baby was something we really wanted or were ready for. I knew I needed time to grieve and heal. Some of the families I spoke with after our experience told us of their desperation to get back in there and try again. They couldn't wait to begin the process of trying for another baby. The unmistakable loss in their lives was too much to bear, their eagerness fuelling their desire to create again and have what they so desperately longed for. For me personally, there was no way in the world I felt ready to try again. I had all of this grief inside me that I needed to shift. My relationship with Trent was having challenges. And above all, I wanted to experience all the love and joy in my next pregnancy. I didn't want it to be overshadowed by the grief I felt for Jack. Nor did I want to feel like I was replacing him with another child out of any kind of fear. I wanted the time to honour him, to honour myself. If and when the time came that we felt ready to try again, we would.

With all of this in mind, instead of holding onto the clothes and material reminders, I decided to let them go. Every item of clothing, every piece of furniture. All of the items could be purchased again, if ever we tried for another baby, but right now, we wouldn't be needing them.

As a way of saying farewell to Jack, we held a small ceremony to honour his life and arranged for our closest family and friends to meet us at one of our favourite places by the ocean. I requested everyone to wear gentle and calming colours—definitely no black. I didn't want it to feel like a funeral but rather a celebration of his short life. Trent and I worked with a celebrant to choose words and verses that expressed how we felt about Jack, although I'm not sure any words could sum up what we were going through after losing him. I also wrote a passage that I read out on the day. It took me a few minutes to find my voice as I stood there in front of the loving crowd. It was important to me, as Jack's mother, to bring voice to the feelings inside of me, to express the love and longing I felt within my heart. I stood there in all of my raw vulnerability and thanked him for being the greatest gift of my life. We spent the rest of the afternoon by the ocean eating, drinking and catching up with our friends.

While the celebration of Jack had been beautiful, the evening took a turn for the worse. During a conversation with Trent the night before, I'd asked him not to get drunk with his mates, as he often did when they came together. I reminded him that this was about Jack, not about us. For the most part, he honoured my request, but later that evening, I saw him with his pants around his ankles dancing to 'The Eagle Rock' on our friend's back deck. I saw red, he had crossed the line after dishonouring our agreement. I understand we all grieve in our own ways, and it can look very different from person to person, but this was an outright display of disrespect not only to me, but to our baby. *Do I really want to be with a man in his thirties who thinks this is fun and appropriate? What if this is an indication of the rest of our lives together? Am I willing to accept this as we move forward?* All I knew for sure in that moment was that I'd seen and experienced enough for one day. I took a short walk home and put myself to bed. I'd confront Trent in the morning after a decent sleep and with a fresh perspective.

Five

Temptation

Temptations present themselves to us in many forms. Sometimes they show up in the human form as a way to seduce us into a state of being we are so deeply longing for. These people knock at our door with their baskets full of tasty delights, our mouths watering as we contemplate taking one. One day, there was a knock at my door, an invitation into temptation. It came at a time in my life when I once again found myself in a state of seeking something more than what I currently had. I longed to feel a deep love and connection to life.

It was a workday, and I was en route to a meeting with a colleague. I heard the ping of my phone and looked at the screen to discover I had received a message via social media from an old friend, a man I hadn't seen or spoken to since I was a teenager. *How random! What a blast from the past.* The message read: 'Hello, old friend.' I was surprised and curious why he was reaching out to me. How he found me and why he had chosen to connect with me at this time in my life. I hadn't seen or heard from him in more than ten years, so it felt a bit strange to be contacted out of the blue. I didn't know it at the time, but responding to the message would lead to the course of my life changing very dramatically in the following months.

The old friend—let's call him Malcolm—was someone I'd met when I was a teenager at Stradbroke Island. I was with a group of friends who'd take their 4WDs over for a weekend of camping and shenanigans. Stradbroke Island was a place we loved visiting; crystal clear water, the opportunity and space to drive on the beach, fish and run amok, doing all the things we loved doing. We were around the campfire one night, laughing and being silly teenagers, when a couple of dudes stumbled (literally) into our campsite. We sensed no threat from them, and being the chirpy gang we were, we invited them in to hang out. I don't recall the exact details of how it all went down, but numbers were obviously exchanged at some point, and our friendship circle grew a little bigger, with Malcolm and his mates joining in.

We shared many adventures together and were always out exploring in our 4WDs, fishing different spots, and engaging in lots of different things with our other friends. One of the stupidest things I remember us doing (though extremely fun at the time) was deciding one night to take gnomes and other various statues from people's front yards to then leave them on other people's front doorsteps. Once the statue was in place at the random person's front door, we would knock and quickly run back to the car that was waiting with one of us filming the reaction of the homeowner as they opened the door to a random (and sometimes huge) statue on their front doorstep. The looks of complete and utter confusion on their faces sent us into hysterics. Little shits.

Back in the day, it was no secret that Malcolm had a crush on me and wanted more than a friendship between us. I don't know what it was, but for me, I was content with just being friends. I wasn't overly interested in boys, men, and relationships. I loved feeling free and enjoyed hanging out with my friends and having fun. Don't get me wrong, as a young woman with insecure tendencies, I enjoyed attention from men, but not enough to make me want to dive into any kind of committed relationship. I wasn't keen on anything more. Plus, I felt Malcolm wasn't really my 'type' at the time. I didn't really *know* what I wanted or was into, but I knew it wasn't him.

Our friendship came to a grinding halt the day he rolled his ute with me in it. We were out one night on one of our silly adventures, this time driving the car in a dark paddock chasing rabbits. At times, we were going so fast, I was sure we would tip over. And then we did. The ute rolled, leaving us upside down in the dark of the night in a random field in the middle of nowhere. Thankfully, we were wise enough to be wearing seatbelts and none of us sustained major injuries. Malcolm and his friend got out first and then kind of left me there to sort myself out. I was so hurt by this that I wasn't able to forgive him for it at the time. Leaving me there felt disrespectful and wrong. We didn't speak for over ten years.

In the weeks following the initial reconnection, we exchanged messages via social media about our lives, our families and what we'd been up to over the last ten years. He'd had a son, worked in a job that required him to live interstate and travel overseas from time to time. He wasn't in a relationship. My curiosity was piqued as to how and why he'd reached out. The timing of it all felt orchestrated. *Did he know what was happening in my life? Why now? Why me? What were his intentions? Why did he care?* I had to know. And so, I put it to him and asked him outright. He told me he'd seen a picture of me at a mutual friend's wedding on Facebook and that he felt like getting in contact. I didn't suspect anything unusual in his response and continued to chat with him as the weeks went on.

One specific message from Malcolm is planted in my memory as it triggered something inside me. I suppose you could call it a whisper of caution and curiosity. In one of our conversations about our lives, he mentioned he saw a photo of me on my wedding day and commented on how beautiful I looked. I thought this was a little strange, considering he hadn't seen me for many years. *Why was he saying this? Where did he see the picture? Why that picture? Why that comment? Why now?* I accepted his compliment as gracefully as I could and moved on, although it continued to niggle at me.

At the time of him reaching out, Malcolm was living interstate. He asked if it would be okay to meet when he was back in town for a brief visit before he departed for his next work project overseas. He was keen to catch up and chat more about where life had led us in the decade that had passed. I felt compelled to meet with him. Something inside of me urged me to go. I wanted to know more, to see what he'd made of his life. And so, I agreed to meet him for breakfast a few weeks later.

I answered the knock. I had opened a door.

In the lead-up to our breakfast meeting, I showed Trent photos of Malcolm and his social media account. I guess this was my way of reassuring Trent he was purely a friend, and for him to know what he looked like and who he was, in case anything happened. I wanted him to feel comfortable and reassured of this just being a meeting between old friends and nothing more. Trent reassured me time and time again he was okay with us meeting for breakfast. I don't think Trent had a jealous bone in his body and was very trusting—qualities I loved in him.

We met at a café in a place where Malcolm and I had visited many times in our youth, mostly to fish and sit on the shore telling stories and planning our next adventures. It was nice to catch up and talk about where life had taken us. I was struck by the differences between us. What became increasingly obvious to me was that we'd walked very different paths. He seemed to be carrying some baggage with him. As I sat across from him, that voice inside me spoke. *Be careful, Jacqueline.* I felt something was 'up' with him. Whatever it was, it felt disturbing and troublesome. His energy was low. I sensed he may be struggling with something or some things in his life. It was a feeling so strong it was unavoidable. I wasn't able to pinpoint exactly what meaning it held at the time. Perhaps you could call this the 'gut feel' or 'intuition' so many of us have in moments like these. What was important to me was the choice to either be still and to listen to the voice that was speaking to me, or to ignore it and carry on.

We finished our meal and went for a short walk along the shoreline. We were chatting away about life and sharing memories of the old days, laughing as we recalled many of the silly choices we'd made in our youth. Then came a moment when we stopped on the jetty and looked out over the sea. Malcolm turned to me and asked, 'So, are you happy in your marriage?' The question caused me to freeze. I felt paralysed by the power in the question. I felt confused why he was asking such a thing after we had only just reconnected. It felt invasive. This part of my life was private. I didn't understand the intention sitting behind the question and what interest he had in my response. It felt like such a strange question to pose at a first meeting after so many years—on top of the comment a few weeks prior about how beautiful I looked in my wedding dress.

This question led me down a path of personal enquiry. It opened doors within I'd closed, not wanting to see the contents of the room inside. When I asked myself the same question, I realised the truth of my situation—I wasn't one hundred percent happy in my marriage. Since Jack's birth and death, a lot had changed. From my perspective, we were struggling to survive the immense grief we each felt in our hearts. Our grief illuminated some of the dark alleys we'd walked down as a couple. It amplified our differences and challenged us to grow together. When I look back now, I can see cracks were forming in our relationship prior to Jack entering our lives. These would only deepen as we continued to grieve in very different ways. It was as if a floodlight shone down on us and illuminated every challenge or pain point that existed in our relationship prior to that moment.

Initially, I would say the experience of Jack's death brought Trent and I closer together in our marriage. It showed us the importance of loving one another through such difficult times, that when faced with such tragedy, there's comfort in the familiar; in the touch or warm embrace of a loved one. We spent a lot of beautiful time together in the early days following Jack's death.

Both the physical and emotional changes I went through as a woman meant I would never be the same person I was before Jack entered our lives. How could I be? Parts of me died along with him that day and created space for new growth and transformation. The life I'd lived prior to this moment was beautiful because I knew nothing more. Jack shone his light into the depths of my own darkness. He gave me the courage to choose to see my life in a different way and explore all of its possibilities. I met Trent in my late teens, and we got married when I was twenty-four years old. My weekends back then had been filled with nights out and partying. I was happy to drink, happy to be the designated driver, and happy to turn a blind eye to the things I heard and saw happening before me that were in complete conflict with my personal values. Perhaps this was my way of conforming to social norms—of being accepted.

Once Jack arrived, I could no longer ignore these things. My tolerance for issues that conflicted with my values and beliefs wore thin. I became *intolerant* to them and unable to stand there and watch as they happened. I chose to remove myself from situations and distance myself from people in my life whose values didn't align, or who made me feel any less than I wanted to. It was tough. It caused ripples that eventually turned to waves. People wondered what was 'up' with me. I didn't know how to explain it and I didn't feel the need to.

This sorting out of my life caused tension in our relationship as I no longer wanted to participate in certain situations that previously wouldn't have been an issue. Specific people began to irritate me. Trent struggled to understand why I didn't want to do the things I'd done before. I struggled to articulate it to him in words. I didn't know why in my head. I just knew in my heart there was more to life. I was seeking to discover what that was. I longed for him to hold my hand and walk beside me as life revealed this to me. Yet, at other times, I felt I needed to venture out on this quest alone. The push and pull were tormenting—parts of me resisting change and other parts craving it.

I was lost.

The woman I once was had become so foreign to me. Like a stranger in a foreign land. I didn't speak the language and I didn't know how to navigate my way around. I had no idea who I really was at my core. And it wasn't until I started learning the language—the language only I could understand—that I began to reclaim my power. It was an uncomfortable time in our relationship, me coming into my power, as for so many years, I had been power*less*. I'd lived in the shadows. I'd been the person everyone else wanted and needed me to be until I couldn't stand being that person any longer. I longed to be me.

Malcolm continued to reach out to me in the weeks following our breakfast. At first, our messages were spread out and random, becoming more regular over time, along with our face-to-face encounters. It was nothing more than friendship. After all, I was married. My loyalty was to Trent. However, if I am completely honest, I felt myself becoming attracted to Malcolm. I felt happy in his presence. He provided an escape from the life I was living. He showed me certain qualities that Trent didn't have. I found myself being drawn to those—refusing to see the other not-so-beautiful qualities lurking in the shadows. My attraction to him caused a lot of internal turmoil, as it felt so wrong to be interested in another man while also being married. *How could I even be attracted to another man? What does this mean? Are Trent and I finished if I am finding myself attracted to someone else? Does this mean I need to leave my marriage?*

I was utterly confused about what I felt, and I didn't know what to do with it all. So, I continued to talk with Malcolm on and off, while working hard to keep my marriage afloat. For how long I would walk with one foot in each camp, I didn't know. Morally, I knew that it didn't sit well with me, or feel healthy to be in this kind of situation. I knew the time would come when I'd need to decide which camp called me more. As time went on, I became increasingly uncomfortable with my predicament. I needed to make a choice, and I needed to do it sooner rather than later.

Six

Deciding

We worked hard at our marriage, enlisting the help of professional couples' counsellors. We had a number of sessions to work through our challenges and our pain. I also had my own individual sessions to do my personal work. We talked. We cried. We vented. Sitting with these people enabled us to talk about things we'd previously struggled to. They helped us open up and voice out the hurts we held inside without the other interjecting with anger or judgement. I'm proud of what we achieved in those sessions.

Outside of the safety of that room and back in the reality of our lives, we struggled to implement any kind of long-term positive changes. How the previous two and a half years had unfolded took a huge toll on each of us. The hustles of daily life led us back into our habits and we would revert back to the exhaustive bickering that we worked on to shift and change. Ultimately, the day came when we decided—together—that our marriage could no longer survive the grief we both felt in our hearts. We could not forgive or move through the resentment and hurt we had imparted on one another.

Three days before Christmas, our marriage ended.

Seriously, three days before Christmas is when you're choosing to do this. Surely there's a better, more convenient time that isn't Christmas. That's the thing about big life decisions and matters of the heart. When it's time, it's time. I could no longer put off what I knew was inevitable. It was almost as if some powerful force—stronger than I'd ever known—had taken over my whole body. *If not now, then when?* I could've found a million reasons not to leave, birthdays, anniversaries, weddings, engagements, deaths, births ... the list goes on. In my heart, I knew it was the right time for me to leave. I couldn't bear it any longer. In the days prior, I would walk around the house looking at all the things we had collected and created together over the years, and I would feel an emptiness and a heaviness in my heart. It was as though there was nothing left within me to give to our relationship. I arrived at a place where the thought of staying was more painful than the thought of leaving. This is when I knew it was time.

We'd shared seven beautiful and fun years together, and created memories and experiences that will stay with me my whole life. Yet the final two and a half years of our relationship were by far our most challenging. I believe that children have a way of amplifying things in life. We'd had some challenges—mostly differences in how we chose to live our lives and what we valued and believed in. I'd grown out of many of the things I'd loved to do previously. I was no longer interested in going out and staying out all night drinking. Trent still enjoyed living that kind of life with his friends. While I was mostly okay with him doing this, it meant that we spent a lot of time without each other, which I wasn't comfortable with. It was frustrating to me as I felt the distance between us becoming bigger and bigger as time went on, yet I didn't want to stop him from doing any of the things he wanted to do. Ultimately, I wasn't able to love him unconditionally.

It was hard for him too. He ran his own business, which needed him to be out of the house six days a week. When he had a day off, he wanted to do the things he loved. More often than not, he would spend his spare time with his friends out on the water. Boating and fishing were his outlet. This was where he found peace.

I struggled to express my longing to spend time together in a useful way, often turning to anger, which inevitably helped no one. I wanted us to do more of the things we loved doing together. How I longed to be on that boat with him! As I watched him prepare for his fishing adventures, all I wanted to say to him was 'take me with you'. Instead of bringing him closer, which was ultimately what I wanted, I pushed him further and further away. Eventually, I viewed everything he did through a lens of resentment. As the months rolled on, I felt as though I lived my life as Jacqueline, while Trent lived his life as Trent—no togetherness—and we met somewhere in the middle for mealtimes.

I realise I'd left our marriage months before I *actually left* the marriage. After speaking to many women in my life who've left relationships, it seems it's somewhat of a common occurrence. It's almost as if the relationship is done in our hearts and minds, and so we grieve the end before the end has even arrived. We go through the stages of grief, preparing ourselves for the moment. And when we finally reach the stage where we choose to no longer continue, it's almost as if it's a relief, a reprieve from the agony we've felt in the time leading to the decision.

In the months leading up to the separation, I was crippled by fear. It was difficult for me to imagine not being in the marriage, not being with Trent. I feared being alone. I concerned myself with all the tiny details, like what I would tell people, and what they would think when they knew. *What would I tell Trent? How would I explain it to him? Would he understand? Did he feel the same?* Then I would overwhelm myself with all the logistical details. *How would we separate the things? Who gets what? What about our money? Where would I live? How do you even get a divorce? Is there a person that can help with that?* I didn't think I had anywhere to go. I didn't expect

my parents to support my decision because they loved Trent, and
I assumed they wouldn't understand. And it went on and on and
on in my mind for many months. I'd cry uncontrollably because
my heart knew what it needed to do, but my head would interject,
casting seeds of doubt and delaying the inevitable. I had to be brave.
I had to dig deep and find the courage to overcome my deepest
fears and leave all that was comfortable and familiar behind. Then
there came a day when the logistics didn't matter anymore.

When I said to him 'I don't think I want to be married anymore',
we sat on the couch and both cried. In our hearts, we knew that
moment was coming. We'd danced on its doorstep a few times
before. It wasn't a shock to us, but it was to many people around
us. After agreeing it was the best decision for us, we leapt straight
into the details of money and the how-tos of separation. I can see
this was probably the shock we felt taking over in those moments
following our decision—our heads taking over. This particular
day in December also happened to be my dad's birthday, a day
usually set aside for celebration. We were due at my parents' home
within the hour. 'What would we tell them?' 'How would we tell
them?' 'How would they react?' These questions dominated the
conversation for the next few minutes, until we decided to just go
there and see what happened.

Within minutes of arriving, we couldn't hold back from sharing
the news of our separation with my parents. Their reaction was
complete and utter devastation. They couldn't comprehend or
accept that this was happening and that we'd reached the final
destination in our relationship. I remember them asking all the
questions. If we'd spoken to someone. If we'd tried everything.
If we were sure. I think this was their way of processing it all. I
can understand how they felt. My family adored Trent, especially
my dad. They got along really well and loved hanging out with

each other as much as Trent and I did. Maybe even more. My dad thought so highly of Trent as if he was a son to him. And I suppose he was, in a way. He was in our lives for almost ten years. We all grew to love him in our own ways. It took my dad a very long time to accept the reality that Trent would not be in our lives anymore in the way he had been before. It was going to take time for us all to come to terms with what was happening and to grieve the end of something and someone so special to us.

We had an annual trip planned for the coming weeks, one in which our friendship circle came together and celebrated the Christmas and New Year period. We agreed we would both still go together. We used this time away to grieve together. We each spent time with our friends, talking and sharing stories. We hugged it out. We cried together. We partied together. Our friends asked us time and time again questions like 'are you sure it's over?' 'You guys seem as though you are still so in love.' And maybe we were. And perhaps it looked that way because in those early days following our initial decision, we spent a lot of time together, doing separation the only way we knew how, and it was beautiful. I spent a lot of time by the ocean over the week, black cockatoos flying overhead as I stared into the sea and cried. Grief and sadness flooded my body, rising like a king tide on a full moon. It filled my body and when I couldn't hold it any longer, it flowed over and out of me.

I decided I'd leave the holiday a week early to go to our home and pack up my things before moving in with a friend and beginning the search for my own place. My friend and her husband were overseas at the time. I felt an immense sense of freedom in the time I spent there. It was the first time in my adult life I'd lived alone. I used my time there to get healthy and focus on myself. I say, 'get healthy'. Eventually, I did focus on my health, after a brief phase of smoking one or two cigarettes a day and indulging in a couple of drinks each afternoon. I'd return from a day at the office, put on some music, pour myself a glass of red wine, light up a cigarette and sit on the back deck and enjoy every last drop and draw. I loved every moment of it and experienced no shame in my choices at the time. I never 'took up' smoking and was always able to stop whenever I felt I'd had enough. I am thankful for this. Perhaps the red wine and cigarettes were my way of rebelling against life—my own version of freedom and not giving a fuck. Or perhaps they served as a kind of anaesthesia, putting me to sleep and shutting me off from the reality of my life and its current set of circumstances. Whatever it was, it felt so good at the time. No regrets.

With this newfound sense of freedom, I also immersed myself in the things I'd always wanted to do. I signed up for the dance class I'd been looking into and dreaming about doing for the last year. I exercised in new and different ways. I had freedom and control over my finances and treated myself to the things I'd longed for. There was a lightness in my body and a soft sparkle in my eyes. I was enjoying becoming this new version of myself and was feeling happy and strong.

In the time following my separation, I let Malcolm into my life. This time as more than just a friend. When I look back, I was too quick to let him in the way I did. It was like I'd just gotten out of one relationship and was immersing myself in another. I saw in him things I'd longed to see in Trent. He showed interest in things I loved and valued. Perhaps the expression 'love is blind' exists for a reason. I had a distorted image of the man in front of me, drunk with the lust I'd been longing for in the years prior.

The perfect little unit soon became available at a place called Runaway Bay. At the time, it seemed like the perfect place to be going—Runaway Bay—considering all that was unfolding in my life. I'd seen the unit advertised online and arranged a morning off work and an appointment with the agent to show me through. I immediately fell in love with the place. It was the right size for me and also had a spare bedroom I could convert to a study or set up with a bed if anyone wanted to stay over. It had polished floorboards throughout and both the kitchen and bathroom had recently been renovated. The area was lovely too, with the ocean only a short ten-minute walk. I even had my own pontoon! Not that I had a boat to attach to it, but it felt like a lovely place to sit on an afternoon with a platter of food and ponder my new world. The rent was expensive and I knew it would be financially challenging to live there alone, but the call was so strong it outweighed any doubts. I went into it with the attitude and mindset that it would all work itself out and that I would be okay.

I used some of my savings to buy a new bed and a lounge. I invested a lot in the mattress, which became known to every person who lay on it as 'The Cloud'. The couch on the other hand, well ... I have no idea what I was thinking the day I bought it. I must have been feeling overwhelmed with the long list of life admin because I didn't even spend the two minutes required to see if it was cushiony enough for me. It was definitely an impulse buy. This couch remains the most uncomfortable seat I've sat on in my life. I would laugh each time someone visited the unit. They'd back up and plonk themselves on it, half expecting to sink into the spongy cushions, yet almost always springing back up to their feet due to the hard-as-a-rock sensation. The couch became known as 'The Rock'.

Each afternoon, I would walk along the foreshore and enjoy the salty ocean breeze, sometimes indulging in a swim, other times, sitting barefoot in the sand. I often had my close friends Sophie and Daniel come and spend time at the unit. We'd go on adventures together, chasing waterfalls, visiting caves, watching movies and sharing many belly laughs. Sophie and I formed a friendship ten years prior when we first met at work. Sophie was my boss, but it hadn't taken long for us to realise we were kindred spirits and formed a strong bond and friendship. We shared many life events together: marriage, divorce, motherhood, career and all things in between. Despite our lives unravelling at times around us, we almost always could sit and laugh together in the face of it all. We taught each other how to be resilient by being the example.

One day, Sophie and I were in the work car park, which was a frequent meeting place of ours and a place of many breakdowns and breakthroughs. I was sitting in the boot of my car on top of many of my life's belongings, one being my wedding dress. My car boot was often an accurate outer reflection of my inner world. And at this stage of my life, my car boot was a fucking mess. There was shit everywhere. Besides my wedding dress, I had no idea what else was piled up underneath it all. I look back at the photo Sophie took of me sitting on top of a pile of my own messy shit in my car boot when my internal world was messy and chaotic, and I smile. I was laughing, coffee in hand, at the ridiculousness of it all.

"Mate, what are you going to do with your wedding dress?" Sophie asked. The beautiful champagne wedding gown I'd worn on our wedding day had been stored in a vanilla-scented, beige garbage bag, in the boot of my car since the week after the wedding. Virtually untouched, covered in red dust from dancing in the barn with patches of dried-up gravy from the midnight roast pork roll scattered all over. Up until this moment, I hadn't given it a thought. *What would I do with the dress?* It felt weird to keep it. I hadn't needed it in all the time that had passed. I certainly didn't feel the desire to pass it on to anyone in my life. And I didn't want to sell it.

So... I decided to burn it.

Doing this felt like the ultimate release and meant I had one less item taking up space in my car boot. I knew I wasn't choosing to burn the dress out of any kind of rage or hurt, as I didn't feel either of those things when I thought about Trent, or our marriage. We'd shared seven beautiful years together with a couple of not-so-glamorous ones at the end. I still feel a deep sense of gratitude for the relative ease and grace with which we separated. Setting the dress alight and watching it burn felt like the right choice for me. I chose the date of the next full moon and invited Sophie and Daniel to join me for a bonfire on the beach.

We waited until dark, until the light of the full moon glistened over the ocean, to begin our walk to the beach carrying with us the essentials: the dress, matches, music and red wine. We chose a spot on the beach and began digging a pit in the sand with our hands. This would become the nest the dress would lay in. Then we took out the dress and set it down in the sand. What had been one of the most elegant wedding gowns now lay in a heap, awaiting its impending death. We poured some wine, turned on some music, and I lit a match, kneeled and set the dress on fire.

I'd imagined a raging inferno of flames. I'd assumed the dress would ignite very quickly and turn to ash in a matter of minutes. The opposite was true. The dress took almost twenty minutes to burn, parts of it burning quicker than others. At times, the flames were so gentle and mesmerising in colour and the pace that they came and went. It was peaceful and beautiful. Then, at other times, the flames raged like a windswept bushfire seeking fuel to keep it alight. We waited and watched patiently as it burned, until there was nothing left. And then we got drunk on red wine.

Seven

Self-Destruction

Malcolm was well and truly part of my life now, with the connection between us growing more intense with every day we spent together. I went from being obsessed with being well and taking care of myself like I never had before to all of my attention being placed on this other person and making Malcom happy. Above all else, there was an undeniable physical chemistry between us, so much so that Malcolm could walk into the room, and my whole body would tingle with anticipation.

As time went on, I realised he wasn't good for me. Despite our shared interests and intense physical chemistry, there were many differences in our perception of life and how we dealt with its challenges. Countless red flags flew in front of me. Sadly, my ability to see them was clouded by the rose-coloured glasses I wore. My decision to allow him into my life and denial to see what was right in front of me, led me down a path of self-destruction and isolation. I became victim to his manipulation and narcissistic abuse. If only I had listened to the whispers when I first heard them. If only I had seen those red flags flapping around, perhaps my story would've been different.

I believed I loved Malcolm when he was vulnerable and gentle with me, and I hung on in the hope he'd be like this all the time. I fell in love with the man I wanted him to be. Who I knew he could be, rather than who he was. And in turn, I was subjected to much pain and torment.

I first started noticing changes in our interactions when Malcolm went back to his interstate base. The changes in our communication was subtle, a passive-aggressive comment here and there catching me off guard. I often thought some of the things he said were a bit strange and often complete overreactions, though I never let them bother me too much in those early days. Over time, these comments became more blatantly obvious, escalating into verbal abuse and blame. We then entered the ultimate game of control. He the master. Me, the puppet.

Living so close to the ocean, I would often return home from a day at the office, dump my stuff at the door and head out for a walk or ocean swim. I always left my phone at home or in the car. Afterall, this was my time to decompress and have a few moments of stillness to myself. I would emerge from the water or return from my walk feeling refreshed and revitalised, having had little to no distractions. When I'd look at my phone, there would be anywhere from five to ten missed calls from Malcolm—often within the space of five minutes. Then there'd almost always be a follow-up text of some kind saying something like: 'Don't want to talk. Okay then.' When this kind of behaviour first started happening, I felt so confused as to what was going on. I had no idea what he was triggered about and spend a lot of time explaining myself, justifying my actions and choices as if reporting to a prison warden on my whereabouts. I'd reassure him that 'yes, I did want to talk to him', but I was out and about enjoying some peace doing something I loved and didn't have my phone nearby. As this behaviour continued, I became exhausted by it all. I shut down. I'd see the missed calls and messages on the screen and allow myself some peace before the impending onslaught of questioning and abuse. *Don't pick up the phone, Jacqueline. Leave it there on the bench.*

Go and have a shower, go for a walk. Leave it. It will all be there when you get back.

He had a constant and incessant need to know where I was, who I was with, and what we were doing at all times. The checking-in with me became a daily occurrence, the only exception being if he was preoccupied himself. When he was out with friends or away camping, I'd rarely hear from him until the following day, or until he was alone again and felt the need to connect with me. I was okay with this, knowing that it was healthy and normal to catch up with friends and do things without one another. Initially, I liked that we each had our own separate lives and some distance between us. Over time, I became less okay with the perceived injustice of it all—of it being okay for him to be free and to be out socialising and living, doing things he loved, but not okay for me. I couldn't understand it. It made no sense.

It became his expectation that I be available to take a call and speak to him whenever he demanded, regardless of what I was doing. He would message me, knowing I was out with my friends or family. In the beginning, it wasn't so bad. I took the calls. I responded to the messages. I was there for him. I didn't want him to feel alone. All my responding and reassuring only supercharged his anger and insecurities. He'd snap at me and ask how I could be out enjoying myself when he was so upset and alone at home. He'd say 'I thought you said you'd always be there for me... Now, you don't have time to speak to me because you're too busy having fun without me.' I felt a growing anxiety, fully aware of the consequences of not answering or missing a call. I would nervously check the screen over and over and over again in case there was a message. If there was, I was even more anxious about opening it, never knowing what the contents would entail. I remember my friend asking me if I was expecting a message or a call from someone as I kept touching my phone all the time. And the answer was always yes. *Yes, I am waiting for the message or the call to come that is intended to make me feel awful about enjoying myself. I don't know when it will arrive, but I know it will.* Twelve months prior to this, I wouldn't have even known where my phone was. So much had changed.

Most of the time, his words were intended to bring me down, to match his own feelings about himself. Even if they were worded in such a way that seemed loving, there was always an undercurrent of manipulation or insecurity. I was able to manage my emotional state well in the early days, but eventually, I found myself buying into his bullshit, leaving me feeling drained and depleted. It became almost impossible for me to enjoy any kind of time away from him, for fear of what that would mean when we reconnected. I chose not to go to things and began to isolate myself from my friends and family, as it felt easier than dealing with his constant questions and abuse.

During our time together, he never wanted to commit, or be in any kind of romantic relationship, though he had no issue manipulating me to believe he did. He'd often tell me he loved me and would fantasise about a future together. Yet he never took the steps to make these so-called fantasies reality. There were several times I'd requested a commitment from him, and each time he found a reason for us not to be together. This confused me no end. How could he say over and over that he loves me, that he could see a future with me, that he wanted to travel and explore and do all of these things, yet not want to actually do any of those things? The game was exhausting, yet I was addicted to playing.

Throughout this phase of persistently checking on my whereabouts and expecting my constant attention and availability, it was extraordinary to me that he refused to acknowledge me as his partner or to commit to anything more than a friendship. Yet each time he felt me pulling away and creating some distance between us, there would be some kind of grand gesture in an attempt to lure me back in, giving me just enough of a glimpse of hope of what could be. I took the bait. Every. Time. The lures became less enticing with time, going from promises of hope to threats of self-harm.

Deep down, I felt he didn't want to be with me and he didn't want anyone else to be with me. I played along for far too long. Parts of me loved parts of him. I clung to those, afraid of what might happen if I let go. I fell for all of the 'gunnas'. 'I am gunna do this with you.' 'I am gunna take you there.' 'We are gunna live together.' Doing all of those things with someone sounded wonderful, so I hung in. I waited and waited and waited. In the end, I gave him the nickname 'gunnaoneday'.

In the almost two years we spent together, I didn't meet a single friend of his other than a couple of people he worked with and his immediately family. I always felt it was a bit strange, considering how much he said he loved me. We were in the car one morning when his mum phoned to say hello. When she asked what he was up to for the day, he answered 'just hanging out with my mate from Toowong'. I wasn't from Toowong. I've never even lived there. I did remember he had a male friend who did. I asked gently why he lied to his mum and the reply would be, 'Er, I dunno'. He always had a reason or an excuse as to why the lie was a better option than the truth. Red flag.

It also seemed a bit off that he didn't want the woman he 'loved so much' to be a part of his life and involved in all the major celebrations of life. He'd often go to the bay islands for day trips with his friends and their partners, camp overnight, go to baby showers, dinners, parties and other social events. I was never invited. When I would question him on this, he would lie to me and say they were boys' trips, only for friends in the social circle or whatever other story he could assemble at the time. I knew these were lies because I used social media to check out what was happening. I believe we all have a strong intuition, especially as women. I trusted my gut when something didn't feel right. I found images of these so-called boys' trips where there'd be kids playing, partners hanging out on the beach—both men and women celebrating. Even the fact that I felt propelled to check out the story should've been enough of an indicator that something wasn't right with the picture, but here I was, yet again choosing to ignore what was right in front of me.

There were days when I would turn off my phone at the end of the day as I didn't want to be woken in the night by his abusive messages or tempted to read them and interrupt my sleep. In the mornings, I'd turn on my phone and there'd be a message or several messages. Some days I would wake up, read them and feel as if the rejuvenated me had been instantly drained of all energy conserved through the night. I'd feel depleted by 8:00am. Other mornings, I'd close all the blinds I'd just opened, make my home so dark and lifeless and go back to bed, turn my phone off and do my best to avoid everyone, and everything.

What frustrated me the most about the whole situation was that I was acutely, painfully aware of the fact I was being emotionally abused and manipulated. I became just as good at the game over time too, able to anticipate his next move as his behaviour became predictable. This wasn't one of those relationships where everyone in your inner circle doesn't like the person, but doesn't tell you, or knows they are bad for you, but doesn't feel it is their place to say something. Countless times my friends would ask me why I was waiting for him and what was I getting from this situation or how was it serving me to feel the way I did. They knew I deserved better. I knew it myself. I often asked myself the same questions. I was so consciously aware of everything that was happening and I chose to keep participating. This frustrated me to no end. *Why was I doing this?* I had no loyalty to him. He had told me numerous times he wasn't willing to commit to an exclusive relationship with me. I should've listened more deeply to what he was saying. 'I don't want to be in a committed relationship with you.' In my desperation to be loved and my obscure view of what could be, I held on for far too long. In a way, I became addicted to the drama of it all. He became the ultimate distraction from me getting on with my life. And I believed I loved him.

I can't tell you the number of times I said aloud to my friends and to myself that I'd had enough and couldn't take anymore—that I was walking away, only to be lured back in somehow to commence another cycle of abuse. I felt so ashamed of myself over time that I stopped telling people I'd entered into another round, or that I had gone back for more of the same. I wouldn't talk about him or about the situation. I began to shut out my closest friends and my family. My mum could sense me distancing myself from everyone important in my life. And Malcolm would say things like, 'As long as we have each other, we will be okay.' In many ways, this reassurance provided a sense of safety and comfort for me, as I felt he was the only person in my life who truly understood the extent of what was happening. Even through our extreme ups-and-downs, there was a bond between us that was growing stronger. I can see now that it was a sick and wounded need to be loved, that we were bonded by our trauma, but at the time, I was none the wiser.

His abuse never escalated into any form of physical violence, though there were certainly indicators this was possible. Physical abuse was written in the pages of his story. He watched his own mother suffer at the hands of her violent husband until one day she up and left him. Days later, he took his own life. He left her alone with two children and a suicide note blaming her for many things that were not hers to own. I could see how this affected him in his life as an adult. I felt for him. Probably too much. Being an empathetic human, I felt it too much. When I was growing up, my mum always said to me, 'You can't help everyone, Jacqueline.' It took many years, and many painful experiences to realise that while you can help a lot of people, you can't help those who don't want to be helped.

The level of control I allowed this man to have over me was shocking. Even now, I still find it difficult to understand how a woman like me could've ended up in a situation like the one I was in. I consider myself a strong and intelligent person. I have a good head on my shoulders. I'd spent the previous three years bettering myself, strengthening my body and mind, deciding what was okay and what wasn't. The ways I gave away my power like I did with him astounds me still, but as we continued on, I would come to realise that what had happened between us in the previous months paled in comparison to what was coming.

Eight

Terminating

I was staying at a girlfriend's place at the time. I noticed my breasts were bigger than normal and felt a bit tender. Sophie and I had shared many of life's big experiences and we found comfort in each other's company. I also appreciated our friendship as we were almost always able to laugh at our own expense. Using humour was our way of coping with the big stuff. And it really helped. There were times when others probably peered through the curtains and got a glimpse of our lives and wondered how we could possibly laugh at such things. But we always did. And we always got through. So, as Malcolm's tiring game of control continued, I decided to spend a couple of weeks at hers because I needed some positive people and influences around me.

Feeling very different in myself and my body, I decided to go out and purchase a three pack of pregnancy tests. I ripped the box open as soon as I walked through the door, went to the bathroom, and peed on the stick. Within what felt like a matter of seconds, two lines appeared. *Pregnant.* The following morning, I took another, and again, two lines, this time a lot darker in colour than the afternoon before. *Fuck.* I kept taking tests for two more consecutive days, hoping there was some kind of error. That it wasn't true. That I was not pregnant with his baby.

Logically, it made sense. We did a thing. A careless thing. Now there was a consequence for that choice. I felt overwhelmed and like it was all too much for me, especially after losing Jack. I worked out a rough timeline in my mind and concluded I was about four or five weeks pregnant. I was very early on in pregnancy, but I was pregnant. I began to burden myself with all the should and shouldn't things. *This shouldn't happen this way. This is not what I want. This man is not a man I want to father my child. This should be a joyful time in a woman's life, a celebration. I am not ready for this. How could I have been so stupid to allow this to happen? What was I thinking? What am I going to do?*

Sophie helped me put things into perspective. She was there for me through it all. Not once did she or her family try to convince me to do anything. They supported me in whatever I chose to do. I knew within my heart from the moment I saw the positive result that I would not be progressing with the pregnancy. That I couldn't sign up for a life with this man. That he wasn't what I saw as a positive male role model for any child.

Though I was certain in my head and heart about all of this, it didn't make it feel any easier to follow through. I judged myself. I projected blame and shame on the situation and on myself as I made the heartbreaking decision to terminate the pregnancy. And I say heartbreaking because I truly felt my heart break a little more in those moments. It was heavy, and it was in pain. I wept inconsolably for many days. I thought about all the couples who try so hard for so long to have children and aren't able. I thought about the little soul inside of me and how I could be so brazen to end an innocent life. I punished myself over and over again. I hated who I was for choosing this, yet I knew in my heart it was what I needed to do.

There are people in my life who will be reading this and discovering this truth for the first time. The immense shame I felt inside held me back from sharing the truth. I was ashamed and afraid of the potential judgements of those closest to me. I had punished myself enough.

Even now, when writing this book, I contemplated leaving out this part of my story for fear of what others may think. It's scary to write about something so polarising. However, I believe there is liberation in making the unseen seen and revealing our deepest truths. There will undoubtedly be people who will pass judgement about the decision I made to terminate a pregnancy. It will conflict with their core values and belief systems—and that's okay. I understand, as it conflicted with my own values and beliefs. I have come to peace with this, for I know that many others will be touched by my speaking of the truth—others who've been faced with the unbearable decision to terminate pregnancies and who've been silenced by their own fear and shame.

I contemplated telling Malcolm about the pregnancy—part of me feeling as if such news would only be a burden to him a month out from departing overseas for work. I also thought that maybe I didn't need to tell him, maybe I could just deal with this on my own like I did with most things. Ultimately, I felt it fair that we at least had a conversation about the pregnancy and were each given an opportunity to express our preferences about how to continue.

I was extremely anxious in the lead-up to the phone conversation, beads of sweat covering the palms of my hands and wet patches forming in my armpits. Malcolm had been unpredictable in his nature, so these were now automatic sensations in my body from never knowing what I was going to get from day to day, week to week. It could be anything from complete and utter rage to a gentle acknowledgment or a loving act of kindness. My anxiety grew from the uncertainty I felt about his response to such news. I was afraid.

My communication style is to say things as they are, whatever they are. Sometimes my words don't shimmer with grace and elegance. They are messy and imperfect but always raw and real.

When he answered the phone, I said something along the lines of 'I have something I need to share with you. I am pregnant'. We had a conversation about what we each felt was right—from our own perspectives. He explained he was about to leave for work overseas, that the timing wasn't right and that he didn't feel ready for such a commitment. I understood where he was coming from. I thanked him for his input. Ultimately, the final decision was mine to make as it was my body. I had already made it well before we began our conversation.

Once I'd fully made the decision to go through with the termination, the next step was to find a place that dealt with this kind of thing. I had no idea where people go for this procedure. I had pictured a dodgy home operating theatre set up in someone's garage. I was convinced I'd leave with some kind of infection. And surely, it would have to be in a well-hidden place, so as to encourage more of the shame, we as women already felt around such decisions. I found a clinic and organised for Sophie to come with me and arranged to have the day off work.

On the morning of the procedure, I felt a sense of certainty. I knew I was making the best decision I could. Yet, I was overcome with a deep sense of sadness. As I sat down in the waiting area, I looked around at the other women. Some young, some old. Each grieving in their own way. The woman beside me wept as she spoke. "I just can't believe I ended up here. I never thought this would happen to me." "I'm so sorry," I whispered, as I reached out my hand to her. Every other woman in that waiting room shed tears as they waited for their name to be called. There was not a dry eye.

A woman called my name and led me to a private room. We sat at a small round table to talk. I think she may have been a counsellor. I'm sure she introduced herself, though I don't recall the details. At times, I was unable to speak, the words not being able to escape through the tight passage in my throat, now completely constricted by my grief. I was inconsolable. I wept as she spoke to me. I could see her sitting there in front of me, her lips moving, but I couldn't comprehend the words. To this day, I cannot recall the details of what was said in that small room. The one and only thing I remember her saying to me as she reached out her hand was 'You know that you do not have to go through with this if you don't want to.'

In the next room I was met by the doctor, who would complete the procedure. First, the doctor explained that she'd need to do an internal examination to ensure I was far enough along to complete the procedure. I didn't know this was a thing. I assumed it could be done at any time. After the internal exam, the doctor confirmed we would be able to proceed and went on to explain what was about to happen. I would be given a twilight sedation, and she would remove the embryo using suction. It would take about fifteen minutes. She wheeled me into another room, where she placed a mask over my face. Tears trickled down my cheeks as I drifted off to sleep.

When I awoke, I began to cry, as if the tears hadn't stopped flowing, even as I slept. As I walked out of the surgery room, towards the exit, two very close friends of mine were waiting for me. One with bone broth for me to sip on and Sophie to drive me home. I was thankful for their love and support. On the way home, we stopped at a chemist and bought a heat pack in anticipation of some slight aches and pains that might arise over the coming days. Sophie stayed with me until I felt settled and well enough for her to leave.

Those first few days following the termination, Malcolm and I had a few conversations about how I was feeling. The heaviness of my heart and shame so severe that I didn't know if I would ever forgive myself. At one stage, as the weekend drew near, he asked if I would like him to fly home to keep me company. I told him it was up to him, but that I was really struggling and could do with his support. He told me he'd look into flights departing on Friday. Friday morning came and I still hadn't heard anything. I checked to see what flights he'd booked and when I would be collecting him from the airport. My heart rate increased as I heard him say, 'I'm not coming'. He told me he hadn't booked flights for the weekend, and that he would not be coming home. As an obvious first response I asked him what he meant and why he wouldn't be coming when he offered to come and be here with me. He didn't want to dip into his savings was his answer. I will never forget how those words made me feel. 'I don't want to dip into my savings'. Like I was nothing. Completely and utterly worthless. Undeserving of his time and attention. How he could abandon the woman he proclaimed to love at one of the most painful moments in her life—a moment that was half his making.

Many hurtful words exchanged in that conversation. I let him know I hadn't planned financially to be paying for an abortion out of my savings account! Yet it was what needed to be done, based on what we both felt was right. Met with abuse his response was, 'Well, seeing as though you can't fucking afford it, give me your bank account details, and I will send you half.' The lack empathy only fuelled my anger toward him. Prior to this, he had never offered to support me financially. I supported myself, physically, emotionally and financially. In the end, I never saw a dollar from him. Despite the heated call, I held out hope the whole weekend that he would come. He had to, surely? And even more so after the conversation about financial and emotional support. He loved me. He would come.

My little unit was part of a bigger complex of eight, and I shared a set of front stairs with the neighbours. From the couch, where

I spent much of the next few days, I could hear footsteps coming up the stairs. That weekend, every time I heard them, I thought it would be him for sure. *He is here. Of course, he's here.* I was convinced he wouldn't not show up after all of this. I lived in a fantasy land, whereby he would surprise me with one of those grand gestures. I hoped. I prayed. Until Sunday came. It was only then I was able to see the truth and come to terms with the fact he was not coming. I had to say it to myself out loud in order for it to truly sink in and for me to accept it. In the moment of realisation, I felt so many things, but above all, complete and utter rage. It coursed through my veins, filling my body before pouring out of me through a flood of tears.

I can't really remember the detail of the conversations we had over the phone afterwards, just that they ended badly. Somehow, the situation was deemed my fault, which had become the norm in the relationship. I was hurt, heartbroken and grieving. He was angry. It was another reminder of what I already knew. He was not good for me.

And despite all of this, I opened the door and let him back in...

It was a month later. I had been doing so well. I had blocked him out of my life on all social media, phone and email. He was so persistent and relentless in his pursuit to contact me, unable to cope with being cut from my life, that he tracked me down via an app I'd used one time a few months earlier to keep in touch with Sophie when she was overseas. A notification came up on my phone. It was a number I recognised, but I didn't know off the top of my head. It took a few moments for it to register. Then I saw the words: *PLEASE ANSWER THE PHONE.* It was him. He'd found a way to get to me. I ignored him at first, and then eventually, he wore me down enough with his relentless need to talk to me. The next time he called, I took it. Enter Malcolm.

We were back in contact and had reverted back to telling each

other 'I love you', speaking almost daily, until it was time for him
to go back overseas again to continue working. I'd had an honest
conversation with him about what we were and were going to be
when he was overseas. I was tired of being this woman on the side. I
wanted to be more. I wanted to be seen and known. Before he left, I
sat him down, and we had a chat. I said that it was my desire to have
clarity, that we are either all in and we commit to a long-distance
relationship, or we choose to be friends and see what eventuates
upon his return. I outlined what that meant for me. I felt I needed
to be extremely clear as to what was okay, and what was not okay
in a friendship. It felt strange to have to spell things out in such a
black and white way to a grown man, but I knew the importance of
boundaries and being crystal clear.

In the end, I put it to him: "I am asking you to decide what you
would like to do. My preference is to be all in and to have a long-
distance, committed relationship with you. I am willing to support
you from afar, to be here and wait for you to return. We've been
acting like we are in a relationship anyway, so let's choose to be in
one. That is what I want. How do you feel? What is your preference?"

"I think we should just be friends. Have fun. Date other blokes
if you want. We will see where we both are when I return," he said.
Malcolm explained how he didn't want to feel any guilt with me
here in Australia waiting for him. He wanted me to live my life.

"Okay, just friends." I confirmed. "What that means is no more
telling me you love me or any of the other things we've been saying
and doing."

"I know," he replied.

That very night, when he was back home, he wrote to me and
told me that he loved me. And the game began again.

As his time living abroad continued, so did the 'I love you', 'I miss
you' words and all the things we'd both agreed we wouldn't say or

do. I started off strong, pulling him up and asking him to honour the agreements we'd made. Then, I gave in. It felt easier to go along with it than to keep pushing up against it. After all, I loved him. Or at least I thought it was love.

Although we'd agreed to only be friends while he was overseas, for the first six or so months, I felt a deep sense of loyalty to him. I chose not to date or even look at another man. My friends, family and even Malcolm would encourage me to put myself out there, meet people, make connections and have fun. At one point, my mum assumed I was gay or part of a cult, because I was going to women's circles and spending more time with the women in my life. I remember her saying to me: "Jacqueline, it is important to spend time with members of the opposite sex, you know." Still attached to Malcolm, though, I sent him monthly packages with all his favourite things to remind him of home and convince him my loyalty was with him. We spoke almost every day over the phone.

Things weren't always peachy when he was away. In fact, there were times when we would end up in an argument, or I'd feel like I had to diffuse a blazing inferno of emotion and calm him. Almost always because of something I'd done. I may not respond immediately to a text, as I was preoccupied. Sometimes I was showering after a long day in the office. Other times I was walking on the beach, or swimming, or at the gym or socialising with my friends. My absence almost always triggered an insecurity in him to the point he would become so paranoid and obsessive about where I was and what I was doing that he would keep calling and texting. By the time I got to my phone, it was that old pattern. A mass of messages and missed calls. The messages with a certain tone to them, an undercurrent of anger. Once again, I felt the need to explain myself to ease his anxiety. After almost ten months of his hot-and-cold behaviour, I was tired. I felt depleted of all of my life's energy. I'd had enough of the game, and I told him so. That's when he made the most shocking declaration and catapulted our relationship into new territory.

This is how the first threat of self-harm unfolded.

He was due to return permanently from his work overseas and would be situated only a twenty-minute drive from me. In the time he'd been away, we were still 'just friends' based on his preferences. One afternoon, he asked me if we could have a Facetime call that evening, but I wasn't available. He asked why. Instead of lying or making up some story, I chose to tell him the truth. "I am going out with a man tonight."

To say that he lost his shit at this would be a complete understatement. Unable to cope with the consequences of his own choices, he went off: "I can't believe you would do this to me so close to me coming home! How could you?" He reminded me that we'd be telling each other how much we loved each other, that we'd been speaking every day. And while it was factually true, it didn't mean I couldn't go and enjoy myself with another person.

I reminded Malcolm of that day in my unit, when he'd made the decision to remain 'friends', and to not commit to anything more; that it was his choice to be friends, that I'd been loyal to him for the best part of ten months, and that it was okay for me to be doing this. "You wanted this," I said. "The entire time you've been away, you've encouraged me to go out with other people, to have fun, to date if I felt like I wanted to. And I haven't this whole time until now, but now that I am, you want to destroy my happiness. I am going out tonight with a man. End of story."

Andrew and I were never going to be anything, as he was only in town for a short period of time before relocating. We both knew it was a bit of fun and enjoyed each other's company in the couple of weeks prior to him moving.

After the call with Malcolm, I got ready for my night out. I'd received abusive messages throughout the afternoon and well into the evening, as well as him continually trying to call me. I wanted to enjoy myself. I deserved to have some fun. And so, I turned off my phone and left it in my bag.

When I switched on my phone the next morning, there were more missed calls and messages. One voice message had him in tears as he spoke about how he'd 'done something really stupid last night' and tried to take his own life. My heart started racing. My body shook as I listened to the message. At this stage, I didn't know if he had the will or desire to follow through with harming himself. Questions raced around in my mind: *Was he being serious in the message? Is he still alive? What if he isn't? Does that mean it's my fault?* While it turned out to be an empty and extreme attempt to control and manipulate me, I didn't know that at the time.

I phoned my friend. He'd dealt with a lot of suicidal people in his life and had experience working with foster children and men and women who'd experienced many difficulties in their lives. I shared with him my concerns and the story of what had unfolded. I shared my deepest fear that if he was to follow through with it, it would be my fault. He calmed me, his voice and his words soothing my sadness. Then he shared his experience that generally, people who talk about suicide the way Malcolm was, typically didn't follow through with it; that it was a form of manipulation and control. He reassured me it wasn't my fault and gave me a few crucial tips that changed the game.

"I want you to talk calmly about it with him. You can ask him where you need to send the ambulance, or if he'd like you to call his family to advise them. Try to get as much information from him as possible." When I finally phoned Malcolm to speak with him about the night before, I was instantly reassured as he answered the phone. He was alive. I asked some of the questions suggested and very quickly, Malcolm came up with all the reasons why he wasn't, or didn't, or couldn't do what he had threatened. I called his bluff, and it became increasingly obvious that the threats were intended to force me into submission.

I'm sorry to say this episode was not sufficient to get me to break ties with Malcolm once and for all. I returned to him many more times after that first threat of suicide, only to be hurt and heartbroken time and time again. I became a woman I didn't want to be around. I couldn't stand the sight of myself. Negativity breeds negativity. I shut out people I loved from my life because I didn't want them to see who I was becoming. I was ashamed to talk about the relationship with my friends because they'd heard me say it was the 'last time' a thousand times before, only to see me tangled up in the web again days later.

And that's the thing, even as I write the word *relationship*, it makes me smile. He never wanted a commitment to me. He never wore the boyfriend label. He was never willing to have a relationship with *just* me. I had asked for this all those months before, and he had chosen to remain just friends. At the heart of it all, I felt he didn't want me, but didn't want anyone else to have me either.

Yet I clung to the hope that one day he might change his mind, that *I* might change his mind.

Nine

Getting Out

Earlier in the year, I attended a leadership breakfast at work with a keynote speaker whose area of expertise was motivation, something I felt was lacking in my own life. I longed for a life that excited me, that had me eager to greet each day with an open mind and an open heart. I knew it was up to me to do the work to make this a reality.

During the workshop, the facilitator handed out colourful workbooks. They were bright and fun, and just looking at them was enough of an invitation to turn the page to see what was within. Essentially, he'd divided the booklet into the key areas of life: relationships, work, finances, health, wellness. Then encouraged you to work through each area, identifying goals and things you'd like to achieve.

One of the key messages conveyed during his keynote was the importance of having something to focus on, look forward to, and feel motivated and inspired by each day. It didn't take long for me to realise what was absent for me: experiences that inspired joy and excitement, and people, places and things that motivated me to *live*. I was aware of a great number of things to be grateful for: friends, family, and life itself. Yet I craved more. I longed for adventure, for learning, for meaningful connections, and to live a more deeply fulfilling life than I currently was.

That evening, I took the workbook home to my little unit and sat on the floor on my yoga mat, which doubled as my dining room table. I filled out as much as I could, not thinking too much about anything before I wrote it down and just following the process. I didn't manage to get through even a quarter of the booklet that night, but the practice of dreaming up my next move had begun. Over the next few evenings, at the end of some long days in the office, I would look forward to returning home to continue filling out the pages. It was exciting to go through the process of looking at all areas of my life and dreaming about a life worth living.

It took about a week to complete the workbook. I then spent some time reviewing my responses and reflecting on all the things I'd dreamed of doing and being. What stood out for me was the dream of seeing more of Australia. I hadn't seen a lot of the land I call home. Australia was a place I wanted to explore. As I sat there, the idea came to me within seconds, as if it had been there patiently waiting for me to notice it. A solo campervan adventure down the east coast of Australia! *Why not?*

If I was serious about bringing this dream to life, I knew I'd need to make some changes. The first major change was my living arrangements. To be able to support myself financially on my adventure, I knew I'd need to save a fair amount of cash, something I didn't feel would be entirely possible in a short space of time while living on my own. I spoke with my parents and shared my dream with them, hoping to move back in and save some money. I can't say for certain, but I am fairly sure that my mum thought I was a lost cause having some kind of quarter life crisis. My dad, on the other hand, was happy to have me home. He always welcomed us kids with open arms and still loves having his children and grandchildren visit. My parents supported my decision and helped me pack and clean the unit. Saying goodbye to the place was bittersweet. I'd felt so much freedom living there and loved the place, but I felt in my heart that this was the next right move.

The day I decided to move home with my parents, I'd had an argument with Malcolm over the phone, and we weren't in a good place. I had loaded the car full of my belongings and was on my way home with thoughts racing through my head. These head-fuck moments had become a common occurrence. My mind was in overdrive. With my attention everywhere but on the road, I suddenly heard a bang, and felt it too! *Fuck, what was that?* I am as hippy as they come, believing in all sorts of things people judge as alternative. And this crash, I honestly believe, was some way of bringing me back into the moment and out of the fuckery in my head. It was just a hard and abrupt path of suffering, rather than a gentler route!

I'd smashed into the back of another car. I got out of my car to meet the woman I'd crashed into, check out the damage, make sure everyone was okay, and to exchange details. As soon as she asked me if I was okay, I broke down, overcome by emotion. The woman looked so concerned that she reassured me over and over that it was all okay, just an accident, that it didn't matter and that our cars could be fixed. I tried to speak through the avalanche of emotion and managed to blurt out, "It's not about the accident. I have a lot happening at the moment."

I didn't go into detail, though I wanted to. I wanted her to know the truth behind the emotion. I wanted to tell her, "This accident is symbolic of the car crash that is my life to date, of a marriage that didn't survive beyond ten beautiful years, of my son who died inside of me, who I never got to meet and create memories with. It's a reminder of the man who abandoned me as I aborted his baby, who never showed up to support me, and who I continue to allow to torture me. It's the fact that I am moving back home with my parents, unable to support myself as an adult. I'm crying because I don't know who I am anymore. I am grieving because the woman

I used to be died a long time ago, and I don't recognise who I have become." That is what I wanted to say to her. Instead, we exchanged details and moved in different directions.

I chose to keep it inside, and I drove away.

That same day, I moved into the spare bedroom of my parents' home and began unpacking my things. It felt as though the place gave me a warm hug when I entered, as if it were saying: *Welcome home, Jacqueline. You can breathe now.*

Living with my parents was a blessing in many ways. I was extremely grateful for them welcoming me back home. It had been over ten years since I lived with them last, so naturally, there was a period of time when we had to learn how to live together again. It was really challenging at times, as I had so much going on inside of me that I wasn't able or willing to share with my folks. Mum and Dad sensed I wasn't my full self, but they didn't push me to share what was happening.

Malcolm was still very much a part of my life, but our interactions were hot-and-cold. Despite this, I was feeling a deeper sense of contentment within my own life, as I had this wonderful solo adventure to focus on. The joy and excitement I felt around my trip helped to balance out any negativity from Malcolm.

It took a few weeks to unpack fully and settle into the place. Once I felt I was grounded there, I began to map out in more detail what I needed to do to ensure my road trip was a success. I began saving as much money as I could, making enquiries on van rentals and exploring the pages of the Lonely Planet's guide to the *East Coast of Australia*. In my downtime, I loved nothing more than flipping through the pages of the book to highlight all the places I planned to stop along the way. I was eager to get going, but before I set off on this mighty quest, there were a few things I needed to sort out.

First, I decided how much time I'd take to complete my road trip.

The length of the trip was somewhat dependent on my annual leave balance and how much money I felt I needed to live comfortably over that period of time. Based on my rough calculations, I concluded five weeks on the road would be a decent chunk to explore and live freely. I had conversations with my colleagues at work and planned the trip to ensure there wasn't too much disruption or workload issues with the team. And then I did it. I picked a random date in February. My solo adventure would commence on Tuesday, 6 February 2017.

Second, I decided on the type of van I wanted to travel in. At the time, I didn't have enough money to buy my own and deck it out, though I would've *loved* that. I'd seen so many inspiring set ups and watched endless YouTube tutorials on how to fit out a campervan. I always felt so inspired to watch young women travellers who'd created their own van interiors. For now, this option was outside of my reach. Instead, I chose to rent a van from a reputable hire company. I negotiated with them and was able to put a payment plan in place in the lead-up to the hire date. This meant I was able to send them a chunk of money each pay cycle, and by the time February came around, I was all paid up and ready to go. I chose a Toyota HiAce, one of those vans with the big high tops where you sleep in the back. I'd later discover you get blown around in these models so intensely on windy days that you swear you could take flight.

Third, I chose my start and end point. To do this, I relied on nothing else other than good old gut feel and intuition, both of which would serve me well throughout my adventure. I'd decided my trip would commence in Queensland at the Currumbin Surf Life Saving Club with a farewell brekkie with my friends, and would conclude at the Grampians National Park, Victoria, close to the border with South Australia.

The thought of waking up each and every morning in a new place, meeting new people, exploring nature and doing whatever the fuck I wanted was everything I longed for in my life at the time. I was so excited, but of course, lots of people came forth with their opinions and unsolicited feedback in the lead-up to my trip. Friends with heartfelt intentions projected their own fears, with comments like: 'You're so brave to be doing this all by yourself. What if something happens to you? Are you going to be safe on your own?' I'd well and truly considered the cost and consequences of those things prior to deciding this adventure was right for me. A desire so strong had busted through any previously held fears because I felt in my heart it was what I needed to do. And then there were those on my support team who had my back and were just as excited about the trip as I was. They were the people I surrounded myself with as the departure date approached.

The learning opportunities were endless when it came to travelling in a campervan. Simple things like changing a tyre were something I was keen to master. I had no idea how to do this and wanted to feel empowered if, in the unlikely event I got a puncture, I could quickly and easily change the tyre. One afternoon, I arranged for my friend's partner to show me how to do it. First, he changed it, and I filmed it with my phone, and then I had a go. It was a little tricky, and a skill that needed some practice, but I felt confident I could do it if I was ever in a situation that called for it. I didn't intend to go off road on the trip. According to the loose plan I was making based on my book highlights, I'd spend most of my time travelling along bitumen or gravel. The chances of anything happening would be pretty slim, right?!

My dad drove me out to the hire yard, which was about an hour from our home, near the airport. I don't recall a lot of what happened at the hire yard, as I was ridiculously eager to get the

show on the road. I spent time shuffling papers, signing documents
and getting an insurance package. I was not anticipating any issues,
but felt it was a sensible thing to do—just in case. I paid about
$1,500 for coverage, which I later discovered wouldn't be enough to
cover the adventures we had planned.

I drove the van home, parked it in the driveway, and started
working my way through it. Opening every cupboard and door to
familiarise myself with what would now be my home for the next
five weeks. I had a tiny suitcase with a few sets of clothes and one
fancy-ish dress—just in case. In fact, one day, my mum came in
and went through the suitcase, pulling everything out and telling
me it wasn't enough, that I didn't have enough. "You need more,
Jacqueline. This is ridiculous."

But I didn't need anything more. I had everything I needed.

Ten

Hitting The Road

The day of freedom and adventure arrived! I said goodbye to my parents before excitedly driving to my sending off party. We'd arranged a small and intimate breakfast with my workmates, whom I'd grown exceptionally close to over the years. I've heard people say to never cry at work or to show any kind of vulnerability, but I've never been able to do that. I've always felt it best to show up as my true and authentic self, no matter the location or the crowd. I believe this is why I formed so many deep and valuable friendships and connections with the people at work. Of all the many intense experiences of my life, they were right there with me, feeling it all, too. Sometimes, it was pure bliss, joy, and celebration. Other times, we took turns sitting on the milk crate in the corner of the kitchen and crying. Sounds weird, and it probably is, but that was us. A bunch of weirdo co-workers and the quirkiest group of friends.

The morning was stunning, we sat out on the balcony of the Currumbin Surf Life Saving Club overlooking the ocean. The sun beamed down and sparkled where it touched the ocean. The salty air was crisp and fresh. You know, one of those mornings that just *feel* great. We shared breakfast, stories and many laughs, and I was showered with gifts like kefir, a headlamp and a whistle, oracle cards, essential oils, a jar full of handwritten quotes, and fresh limes. All of these gifts were accompanied by the most heartfelt, handwritten letters and well wishes. These people. This day. I was so happy and grateful for all of it.

After we'd finished breakfast, some of the crew headed back to the office to start their day while John, Sophie and I sat in the back of the van for about an hour, talking and laughing. We spoke at length about how cool it would be to own a van ourselves and how we felt we could all very easily go on to live a very minimalist life, not needing much to feel happy. We fantasised about the kinds of freedom we longed to feel, to be free from the hustle and bustle of corporate life, to live how we always imagined we would. Then we hugged it out, said goodbye, and vowed to keep in touch. The goodbyes had a finality to them. Maybe they were wondering, like I was, whether I would return to the corporate world after experiencing such freedom and adventure. I was experiencing the seven-year itch we often hear about in relationships, the popular belief that happiness in a marriage or long-term relationship declines around seven years. I'd always sensed that there was more for me outside of corporate life, and this was my time to explore what else existed beyond the office walls.

I drove down the highway, tunes blaring, me singing in the most unpleasant tones, not giving a single fuck. The Red Hot Chilli Peppers, David Bowie, Queen—only the greatest road trip tunes would be played on this trip.

With no plan or booking schedule, I was unsure where I would stay on my first night. *Yamba sounds good.* I drove there and pulled into The Blue Dolphin Holiday Park, where I went on to stay for a couple of nights. It was a big holiday park, the kind of place set up for families. Once I'd paid for my stay, the woman showed me on the map where to park. "You can pick any site you like in this area," she said. I chose R3—a nice shady spot with a view of the ocean.

Along the way, I learned many things that would make my trip feel that little bit more comfortable. Parking the campervan beside the concrete slab of the pitch was one of my first lessons. Doing this limited the dirt and mud coming into the van. Next, I had to figure out how to hook up the power, a task I felt a bit intimidated by but overcame very quickly once I knew what was involved. These seemingly minor achievements gave me a sense of empowerment and a belief I could do anything.

The day was nice and warm, so I headed over to the pool and chilled out for an hour or so in the afternoon, before heading back to my site for some more rest and relaxation. As I sat in the back of the camper, an older gentleman and his wife walked over. Bob and Mary were grey nomads travelling around Australia in their caravan. We had a brief conversation before Bob ducked off to get something. After a few minutes, he returned with a big book called *Camp 7*. He flicked through the pages showing me all the free campsites and other attractions they'd visited on their travels. We shared a few laughs and many stories. Mary opened up about her life and shared with me her devastation at losing both of her parents in a bushfire when she was eighteen. It was intense to talk about such things with a stranger, but it was the kind of meaningful conversation I'd come to love and appreciate.

Talking with people like this, particularly the older travellers, became one of my favourite things on the road. When people learned I was travelling alone, it almost always sparked a curiosity within them, and they seemed eager to know more about my story. A young woman travelling solo in a campervan seemed like such a foreign concept to many, especially those from different generations. Towards the end of our conversation, Bob went on to tell me that he would never let his daughters drive one of 'these vans', referring to my HiAce. "They're just so short at the front and that's where the engine is. If anything was to happen, they'd end up with broken legs. They're so dangerous these things. Top heavy too."

I laughed. "Thanks for the injection of positivity, Bob."

After such an inspiring and relaxing day, I was definitely not down for the effort of preparing a gourmet meal for one, so I decided on a simple platter of cheese, olives and gherkins.

The rest of my days in Yamba were as spectacular as the first. One of the highlights was a seven-kilometre hike I did in the heat of the day. I was super excited as I had purchased a pair of Merrel hiking shoes specifically for the trip and was keen to get them on my feet and explore nature. I've always felt a deep peace walking in nature. The silence, the solitude. Being alone with myself and my thoughts. I loved it all. I packed a trail mix, water, and a few other essentials into my small backpack and set off along the trail. As I walked along, I was immediately struck by the beauty of the wildflowers that lined the path, and what seemed like hundreds of butterflies all around me. It felt as if they were blessing the path before me. With the first few steps I took, emotions began to rise within me, all the happenings of the previous weeks, months and years beginning to swirl around—wanting to be felt, wanting to be let go. This is one of nature's greatest gifts—the invitation to stillness.

I arrived at Dirragan Lookout with its panoramic views of the ocean and the coastline, the scenery so beautiful it moved me to tears. I slid off my backpack and rested it on the small wooden bench set off to the side of the trail before walking back to face the ocean. As I stood there looking out into the vast open space, I felt compelled to scream. I'd always wanted to stand atop a mountain or someplace deep in the wilderness where no one else was, and let it rip. And although this wasn't a mountain, I felt the urge.

As much as my body wanted to let it all out, my mind got in the way. I began pacing around and procrastinating about what

I so longed to do. *You want to scream. Just scream! Let it out. Do it. There isn't a single person within kilometres of you. What are you afraid of?* I stopped pacing and gave myself one of those pep talks. *Jacqueline, you didn't come all of this way to not do the things you've always wanted to do. Just fucking scream. Let it out. Who gives a shit? What are you waiting for?* And with that, I turned to face the ocean once more, took in a deep breath, opened my mouth, and let out an almighty roar. The sound was so unfamiliar and came from somewhere deep within. It was as if everything I'd stored inside and hidden away had been found and let loose. It felt primal. I felt liberated. And as that moment passed, I turned, walked over to the bench, put my backpack on and laughed hysterically.

The next stop on my trip was a little town named Red Rock, where the river was a beautiful turquoise colour, almost as if someone had painted it with acrylics. I took a walk up to the headland, covered in deep earthy red rock, and noticed a plaque by the boardwalk. Its words honoured the indigenous, traditional owners of the land who were massacred many years ago. These people were chased from their camps, their homes, along the river and up to the headland, where they were then killed. The rocks bleed with the grief of these men, women and children. I took my shoes off at the headland, and I felt deeply for them and the injustice of it all.

After a very emotional hour, I walked back down to the river and felt compelled to get in. The current carries you to the mouth of the ocean, if you let it, and I was keen to give it a go. I went back to the van to change, left my keys with the local fish and chip shop and went to the riverbank. I entered the water carefully and paddled out until my feet no longer touched the safety of the ground. Then the current collected me. It was so powerful that I resisted it at first, doggy paddling and panicking, fearful of its strength. Afraid it would take me under and out beyond any point of return. And then

I reminded myself to breathe. I gave in. I surrendered. I lay flat on my back, gazing up at the sky, and allowed the water to carry me. It was magical.

My adventure continued in the following weeks, visiting Crescent Head, Scotts Head and South West Rocks. I was delighted when I arrived at Port Stephens and paid twenty dollars for a powered site for the night. The owners of the park told me about some sand dunes behind the property, the biggest in Australia, that played host to the cast and crew of the war film *Sahara*. I couldn't wait to get out there and explore the dunes. I hadn't been to the desert to know what it looks and feels like. I'd only been afforded the descriptions given in movies and books. Standing there, I felt like I'd been transported to another part of the world or possibly even another planet. It was unlike anything I'd ever seen. An endless wonderland of soft sand, peaks and troughs. No clear beginning or end to it all. Apparently, people had set up tin sheds in the dunes with piles of scrap metal throughout the place, but I didn't go deep enough to witness those. Still, I took my time, spending a couple of hours exploring. I ran up and down the dunes like a small child filled with boundless energy and excitement. It was another moment and feeling of complete freedom.

I travelled further down the east coast, stopping at many more beautiful places before heading inland to Canberra—partly to see the war memorial and mostly to pick up Malcolm from the airport. I had agreed to collect him and invited him to join me for a small portion of the trip along the Great Ocean Road. It is a gorgeous stretch of coastline in Victoria that neither of us had seen. I thought it might be nice to have some company and explore this part of the coast together. I didn't know it at the time, but this decision would be a crucial error in my own judgement and one I'd regret as the days went on.

After the initial excitement of seeing one another had passed, it took about a day for the joy to be overshadowed by anger and jealousy. Arguments started between us over my choice to go on a few dates with Andrew while he had been overseas. The subject dominated our conversations. We had already revisited it many times over, and he couldn't and wouldn't let it go. It was exhausting to me to be going over the same thing time and time again, to be saying all the things I'd said before, to still not be heard.

One day on our travels back towards the coast happened to be the anniversary of baby Jack's birth and death. I remember telling Malcolm that I couldn't predict how I'd feel but would likely need my own time and space to honour Jack and myself. He assured me he wouldn't get in my way, that it was my day, that he respected my wishes. "Do anything you need to do," he said. I should have predicted things would work out quite differently ... On the day, I was listening to a relaxing playlist, shedding tears as I remembered Jack. He turned to me as my tears fell. "Maybe if you stopped listening to fucking sad and depressing music, you'd stop crying."

I was enraged. How dare he attempt to take this moment away from me or to make it anything other than what I wanted or needed it to be? I turned my head away in utter disbelief, my sadness only deepened by the malice I heard in his tone as he dismissed me. I sat in the passenger seat, feet resting on the dash, my body curled up in a ball.

In the turbulence of the next two weeks, we spent travelling together, I experienced many more moments of deep sadness, rage and regret, alongside sharing moments with Malcolm of sheer joy and relaxation.

His temper was triggered yet again by a very innocent message that he had seen the night before on my phone. Andrew had been checking to see how I was going on my trip. *How did Malcolm even get into my phone to see the message?* It took me a few moments to work it out. A couple of days prior, we'd boarded a ferry to a beautiful place. I was driving and needed quick access to the prepaid ticket in my email. To get there, I needed my passcode to be entered, so I called it out to him, and he typed it in. I assume he had kept it in the memory bank for a moment when I wasn't around, a moment when he could invade my privacy and feed whatever paranoia he had going on.

So here I was, in the shower, getting ready for dinner one evening, when seemingly out of the blue, he started questioning me about Andrew. The questions turned into what felt like an interrogation. I felt bombarded with questions fuelled by his suspicion. It soon became apparent to me that he'd looked through my phone at some point during the trip. From my perspective, there was nothing to hide, but the invasion of my privacy triggered me. The lack of trust and the paranoia he projected my way was so intense. *Why couldn't he let it go and move forward? Why must we revisit this topic of conversation over and over?* After almost an hour, we finally agreed to go and enjoy our evening together.

I'm afraid to say it all surfaced again the next day. I was completely exhausted by the conversation. I'd said everything I needed to say about this matter and wanted to move on. There was nothing we hadn't talked about, no element we hadn't covered. Malcolm started with the usual comments like, 'I can't believe you did that to me. You knew I was coming home soon, and you went on dates with him'. My response was always the same, this was something he'd encouraged me to do, he chose the path of friendship over a committed romantic relationship. Reminding him of his choice only enraged him more and never ended well for me. On this particular day, we had to pull the van over mid-trip. I was crying hysterically after having been on the receiving end of his relentless abuse for over an hour. He sat there as I wept, seemingly emotionless, with a look of disgust on his face. By the time we arrived at the destination, my eyes were puffy from crying. I got out of the van and told myself to move forward and enjoy this part of the coast I'd been so excited to see. I marvelled at the beauty of it all. I cried as we walked. I sobbed at the beauty surrounding me, and at the regret and shame I felt for inviting him to be there with me. I wanted him to leave. To leave this trip. To leave my life.

We continued along the path to a lookout, overlooking the Twelve Apostles. I was still upset and feeling deeply hurt by his anger. And then he turned to me and asked me to make it 'official', to commit to being in a relationship together. I couldn't cope with the absurdity of it all. I felt so close to some kind of nervous breakdown after the conversation in the car, where we'd revisited the topic of Andrew for probably the twentieth time. I could barely see out of my puffy eyes, and he had spent the last hour berating me and projecting his anger. Now here he was, asking me to be his girlfriend. *What the actual fuck?* In a moment of clarity and with conviction, I declined.

The emotional rollercoaster continued for a few more days before the time came to take him back to the airport to fly home, while I would be continuing with my travel plans. I ventured off the coastal roads and into the city to make this happen for him. On this occasion, I was more than happy to make an exception from sticking to the coast road as I'd planned. The moment he left the van and walked towards the airport terminal, I felt instantly relieved. My whole body softened. I exhaled as though I'd been holding my breath the entire time he'd been with me. I felt free to return to myself. "Thank God for that," I said aloud.

Eleven

Moving On

I'd seen many photos of The Grampians, known for its natural beauty, Indigenous rock art works, waterfalls and hiking trails. I was keen to go there and venture off on my own. I looked forward to the return of the feeling of freedom as I hiked in nature again. The welcome pause from life's challenges. The solitude, the silence, the time to be alone with myself and my thoughts.

I spoke to an elderly woman, another grey nomad, one afternoon in the swimming pool of the caravan park we were staying at. I shared with her my desire to see The Grampians and do one of the many hikes I'd seen in the guidebooks. She and her husband had visited many times. "We always stay at a place called the Halls Gap Holiday Park," she added. "It's lovely." I made a mental note and swam a bit more before heading back to the van for the evening.

The following morning, I woke early and packed up the van, ready to start the drive out. I typed The Grampians into the Navman, and it suggested taking me to the *centre* of the national park, which I assumed would be fine. I was always somewhat of a spontaneous traveller, knowing the destination but never really taking the time to stop, research and plan before I set off. This meant I never booked a single place in advance throughout my whole road trip. I'd just rock up and find somewhere with an available site for me to stay. While this had served me well on my travels up to this point, it would prove otherwise when I arrived in The Grampians.

I felt an underlying restlessness the whole morning on my drive out to the national park. I couldn't pinpoint at the time what it was all about, other than to say it was a feeling of unease and uncertainty. I assumed it was just an emotional hangover from the previous week and a half spent with Malcolm, and that perhaps I needed to work a little harder at letting go of him to enable me to enjoy what little time I had left on my trip. I travelled along dirt roads for hours before finally arriving and entering the national park. I drove in and around the place for nearly four hours without seeing any other form of life other than trees; not an animal, not another car, not another human. Being a super spontaneous and somewhat naïve traveller, it was only later that I discovered this national park was over 160,000 hectares in size. I'd have to travel a fair distance before reaching the centre, where the Navman was taking me.

So here I was, having done no prior research or planning for my trip, going only off my conversation the day before with a stranger in a pool at a caravan park and innocently heading into the wilderness. After those four long hours, the Navman calls out "ARRIVED". I pulled over on the side of the dirt road. *Arrived?!* I was filled with confusion and bewilderment. *I am in the middle of fucking nowhere!* What I had assumed would happen was that I would drive into the national park, and there would be a central location or point where I would park the van, then choose from a map which hike best suited my fitness ability and available time— like most of the national parks I'd visited. There was nothing of the sort where I'd pulled over. I had full battery on my phone but no mobile reception. *What the fuck am I going to do here?!* I sat for a few moments, looking around at the thick, dense bushland surrounding me, then I remembered my conversation with the lovely woman the afternoon prior. *Right,* I said to myself. *I'll get myself to Halls*

Gap Holiday Park and figure out the rest in the morning. I reached for the Navman and typed it in. It looked to be about sixty kilometres away. I freaked out a bit as it was getting late in the afternoon, and I had a rule to be off the road and settled in my accommodation for the evening no later than 3:30pm. The Navman had me arriving at 4:30pm. I told myself it was okay, as I knew I would be safe once I got there. I would settle in and talk to the park owners about the hiking tracks in the morning.

I began following the cues of the Navman, but something felt off. It seemed to be taking me deeper and deeper into the bush. Although I didn't know where I was, I felt intuitively like I was heading in the wrong direction. After about half an hour of driving, it directed me to take a right turn down a road that had a gate with bright yellow sign across it saying, "ROAD CLOSED".

"For fuck sakes," I said aloud. I didn't feel comfortable taking the chance of travelling down the road because I didn't know the terrain and what potential hazards I'd be met with, so I did a U-turn, assuming the Navman would re-route and find another way as it so often did when I'd taken a wrong turn or missed a turn in my travels. Over and over, it kept telling me to turn around and travel down the closed road. I calmly explained to the device that the road was closed, and I needed it to find another way! She persisted. "Make a U-turn, make a U-turn". Things escalated quickly, and I began shouting. Eventually, I was reduced to tears. "I can't go down that road," I yelled, "IT'S CLOSED!" The Navman kept ordering me to turn around—the voice repeating itself like a broken record.

I am lost. I am lost in the Grampians National Park, and I am lost in my life in general. Where am I? What am I doing? Somebody please help me. Please help me get out of here safely. Please keep me safe. I don't know where I am.

It took a few moments for me to calm down and stop crying

before I decided I would drive out the way I'd come in, stay somewhere overnight, and decide on my next move in the morning. I knew it would be a long drive out, as I'd spent four hours getting in that morning. The speed limit on these dirt tracks was one-hundred kilometres per hour, which astounded me. Probably because I was a cautious driver, I couldn't grasp travelling at that speed on a dirt road. Mostly, I travelled at around sixty to seventy kilometres per hour. I went over what is called a washboard on the road, where corrugations form across the surface due to moisture and stress from the elements. When you drive over one of these, if severe enough, they can cause your vehicle to shake from side-to-side. As I drove over this particular section of road, I felt the van vibrate intensely, then the back end of the van flicked out to one side and swung back over to the other side. It was thrashing back and forth, becoming more out of control with each passing moment. There was very little I could do to correct what was happening. Truth be told, I didn't know how. This wild beast of a van whipping back and forth with me at the controls.

So, with little choice, I did what I'd practised many times prior: I surrendered to it all. *Jacqueline, this van is going to roll.* And I took my feet off the clutch and the brake, grabbed hold of the bar above the window frame, curled into a ball, and I closed my eyes as I braced myself for what was to come.

An almighty BANG.

The driver's side hit the dirt first, the windows shattering to a thousand pieces, dirt and broken glass rushing in and covering me. Then over I went again, this time rolling to the other side, then once more on each side before the van lost momentum and stopped. It landed upright in a small ditch on the side of the road where the reflective indicator poles line the road as a guide. The engine was still running.

I checked myself over with my hands. I knew I wasn't badly hurt, had no broken bones and hadn't hit my head. There were a few minor cuts and a few bits of shattered glass in my arms, but aside from that, I felt okay. Hearing the sound of the engine running gave me hope. *Sweet.* I will just reverse out of here and keep on driving as planned. I reached for the gear stick and put her in reverse. Nothing but the sound of the engine revving and declining my efforts. I turned off the ignition and got out to take a closer look at what might be happening. The tyre at the back of the van on the driver's side was fully elevated and not touching any part of the road at all. I knew the van would need to be either pushed or pulled out of the ditch, for it to be driven again.

So, I did what any petite young woman with adrenaline coursing through her veins would do. I walked around to the front of the van and began to push. I grunted as I struggled with the enormity of it all. Perhaps you can guess what happened next. The van didn't budge. Not even an inch. It stayed stationary, all 2000kgs of it, forcing me to come up with another way. My next idea was to get my phone and call for help. I opened the driver's side door and reached over into the centre console, but my phone wasn't where I'd left it. It must have been thrown around while I was rolling. I searched through the cab looking for it, but it was nowhere to be seen. For the first time since the accident, I began to panic. The phone, I believed, was my lifeline. My way out. And I didn't know where it was. I started pacing around the van, searching the ground, sifting through my belongings. *Please help me find my phone, please, please, please*, I begged. I don't know who I was speaking to as I asked for help, but it helped to feel like I was talking to someone, or something. Within moments something caught my eye, a small piece of amethyst crystal I placed on the centre of my bed each morning glistened as the summer sun kissed it. I walked over and picked it up, and underneath it, lying face down in the dirt, was my mobile phone.

I immediately picked it up, dusted it off and began dialling 000— the emergency services number here in Australia. Although I had a full battery, I had no mobile phone reception, so the call couldn't connect. Then I remembered the number 112 so many people talked about in case of an emergency. From what I'd heard, this was an emergency number you could call, anywhere, anytime, regardless of available reception. I typed the numbers into the phone, and the word 'dialling' came up on the screen. I sighed with relief, but the momentary respite I felt was very quickly overshadowed by the fact that there was no dial tone. I hung up and tried again. Same thing. Over and over, I tried with no success. *Why is this happening? What is going on? How am I going to get help? And from where?*

Sheer panic set in as I came to terms with my current situation: no one knew where I was. I hadn't shared this part of the trip with anyone. I had no mobile phone reception. The van, which was my mode of transport, and my home was stuck and stranded in a ditch on a dirt road in the middle of the Grampians National Park. It was getting late, and the last time I'd looked at the Navman, Halls Gap Holiday Park was still sixty kilometres away—at least an hour by car. I'd covered some distance since then too. I paced back and forth, continually dialling 112 in the hope that by some miracle, it would connect. *What am I going to do? What the fuck am I going to do?*

I've read that in these kinds of situations, the best thing you can do is to stay put and wait for help. I understand and appreciate this logic, but on this day, something inside me was telling me to leave the van where it was and walk to find help. Everything inside of me told me to get out of there. Remember, I hadn't seen another vehicle or person for a minimum of four to five hours by now. I was in the thick of the Australian bush with no way to contact anyone for outside help. My family and friends had no idea where I was. I'd spoken to my parents a couple of days earlier, but they weren't aware of my spontaneous plan to travel to The Grampians. The thought of staying came and went in an instant. There was no question. I decided to walk. I gathered a few items from the van to take with me; basically, the things within my reach that were still intact, and that I deemed essential for my walk. My small black backpack was still resting on the passenger seat of the van and contained some essential items like a torch, headlamp, mosquito repellent, and a pocketknife. I slid the back door along and noticed the contents of the van had literally been turned upside down. The bed I neatly made every morning was a mess. The mattress, pillows, bedspread and other items gathered in a heap to one side, covered in dust and dirt. The small gas stove I cooked on had been ripped from the bench. Pasta spirals covered the floor as the pantry doors had flung open in the accident. The contents mixed in with the deep orange dust and scattered all over the floor. Through the mess, I managed to find half a bag of trail mix and about 600mls of water remaining in a 10L container.

I went back into the main cab and detached the Navman from its holder. I wanted to take it with me, not because I intended to use it, but rather because I didn't want anyone to steal it as it wasn't mine, and I'd be liable for the cost of replacing it. I laugh at these thoughts, as I recall them. Like, never mind the van you've just rolled, worry about the Navman being stolen by one of the many people you *haven't* seen today. I grabbed my hat, slung my backpack over my shoulder, and began to walk. I walked in the direction I'd been driving—the supposed way out of the bush. My goal was to try and get to the Halls Gap Holiday Park—sixty kilometres, a short twelve-hour walk through the thick bush. I had no idea where it was, or how to get there. *Am I even walking in the right direction? Do I have to make any turns? How will I know? What if I don't make it?* These were just a few questions swirling around in my mind as I ventured off in pursuit of help, riddled with uncertainty.

After a few minutes had passed and I'd had time to think a little more, the enormity of the situation began to consume me. Three main thoughts came in those initial moments, and they were not at all helpful.

The first was that the bush was going to catch on fire. All my eyes could see everywhere I turned was thick, dense bushland. It was a hot Australian summer's day—about thirty-two degrees—and not a cloud could be seen as I looked at the sky. I felt like this tiny, little, speck of a woman in a gigantic space. The fear of being so small, so lost, and so unprepared took over. I was convinced I would burn alive.

Next, I thought that someone was going to jump out of the bush and murder me, as if they'd been waiting patiently in the middle of nowhere for a young woman to get lost, have an accident and walk to find help. I walked cautiously, looking over my shoulder in case said stranger lurked in the shadows.

And finally, probably the scariest thought for me at the time was being alone in the bush at night. I feared the dark. It was getting late in the afternoon, and I knew it would only be a couple of hours before the dark of the night would set in. I thought again about my last glance at the Navman before everything turned to shit. I knew I was at least an hour's drive from Halls Gap Holiday Park. An hour's *drive.* Converting that drive time to steps, and even though math was never one of my strengths, I calculated I would be walking well into the dark of the night.

As the panic grew legs, I looked down at my own and decided I'd make it all go a bit quicker by running. I was in pretty good physical shape. I was fit and healthy and I thought it would be a good idea to make up some time and cover some metres by alternating between running and walking. I'd run for a bit and then slow down and walk, then run some more and then reduce speed down to a power walk. Pretty quickly, I became saturated in sweat and short of breath. I stopped and reminded myself I only had 600mls of water on this thirty-something degree day and a long journey ahead. I chose walking from then on.

As I continued down the dirt road, 112 still dialling on my phone with no successful connection, I noticed a blue sign with a picture of a tent, indicating a campground. I turned right and began to trek down the road where the sign was pointing while yelling out for help. "HELLO. HELP. IS ANYONE THERE? HELP ME. PLEASE HELP ME." I had no idea for how many kilometres this road continued before reaching the campground or if anyone would be there when I arrived. I couldn't see the end of the road, but something in my gut told me to turn around and head back out to the 'main road' I'd been driving along. When I got there, I sobbed uncontrollably. Perhaps the adrenaline was wearing off as the reality of the situation began to sink in.

I looked up at the bright blue sky, reached my hands above my head, palms facing one another, and pleaded. *Please help me,* tears streaming down my cheeks. *I know I haven't seen a car all day, but please send a car. Please send a car, please send a car, please send a car.* I repeated the request over and over and over as I walked and wept some more. I didn't know who, if anyone, was listening. I just kept at it. Hoping. Praying for a miracle.

Half an hour went by like this, when suddenly, I heard a car. The sound was faint, but it was unmistakably a car. The acoustics of the bush can sometimes make it difficult to know where certain sounds are coming from, and I couldn't tell where the car was in proximity to me or if it was even headed my way. So, I changed my plea. 'Please come this way, please come this way, please come this way.' As the last plea left my lips, a white 4WD drove into view, coming towards me, another car trailing behind it. I ran into the middle of the road and fell to my knees, raising my arms into the air, gesturing for them to stop.

They pulled up, and a man and woman got out of the first car and ran over to me, followed by another couple from the car behind. "Are you okay? Are you hurt? What has happened?" they asked, helping me to my feet. I was inconsolable, crying hysterically, unable to speak through the tears. "It's okay, love," they said as they took me to their car, helping me into the safety and comfort of the back seat and handing me an ice-cold bottle of water. It was refreshing. It was what I needed in that moment to bring me back, to calm me enough to speak.

After a few minutes, I found my voice. "I had an accident and rolled a van I was driving. There is no one else with me. From what I can see and feel, I am not badly injured, but the van isn't in a good way," I said. They asked me if I could take them to the site of the accident. "It's just a bit down this road," I explained. "I haven't made any turns on foot." We pulled up beside the van, and the blokes got out to have a good look at the damage, to see if there was any way we could pull the van out of the ditch and get it going again. With the gear they had on board, the four of them were able to hook it up and free it from the side of the road. We were all surprised to discover there were no busted tires, and the engine still ran! We agreed that one of the guys, Keith, would drive it back very slowly, with one 4WD leading the way and the other following closely behind the van in case anything happened. Keith, God love him, was a tiny pocket rocket of a man. He was shirtless and skinny, parts of his ageing brown skin decorated with tattoos, his brassy blonde hair pulled back into a ponytail. A rough diamond, you might call him, and a man with a heart of gold.

As we assembled our little convoy, they came up with a game plan, which they shared with me. "We will take you back to the place where we are staying. Hopefully, you can stay there for the night and then be able to figure out what to do in the morning." On our way out of the bush, we all communicated by two-way radio, sharing many laughs with Keith, who made jokes about the dodgy aircon in the van. He drove the busted van for an hour in the heat of the day, shattered glass and dirt covering the driver's seat, window frames hanging off the side of the thing, and the roof caved in. He was my hero that day. Peter, who was driving the other 4WD, phoned through to the accommodation to advise them of what had happened and arranged for the emergency services to meet us there.

After just over an hour in the car, we arrived at the place they were staying. It was Halls Gap Holiday Park, if you can believe it— the exact place I had been trying to get to earlier in the afternoon. We were met by the police, ambulance, the SES and fire brigade. As we pulled up in front of the holiday park, a policeman came over, took a few personal details, and began questioning me about the events that had unfolded. I was checked over by an ambulance officer, before being taken to the local hospital, another forty-five-minute drive away.

On our drive from the accident to the holiday park, Cheryl, Keith's wife, had shared with me that it was a long weekend in Victoria, and the holiday park was often fully booked. Of course, I hadn't factored in any of this and had no idea what I was going to do for accommodation that evening. I asked the ambulance officer if it would be okay for me to stay the night at the hospital, as I had nowhere to go, nor did I have any friends or family in the town. He reassured me that everything would be okay and encouraged me not to worry about those details.

About ten minutes out from the hospital, I received a message on my phone from a number I didn't recognise. It read:

> Dear Jacqueline,
> My name is Clementine. Together with my husband, I own Halls Gap Lakeside Tourist Park. I am so sorry to hear what happened today. But so happy you landed in the beautiful hands of the people who found you. You will have a bit to digest. I just wanted to let you know that we have put a cabin aside for you in case you get back here to Halls Gap. An envelope with your name on it is at the front door of reception in a wooden box. If you really need to, you can call us, no problem! Your keys to the car are safe with us...If we can do anything at all, text me! For now, rest up!
> Best wishes,
> Clementine

I exhaled in relief and gratitude. *What a beautiful woman.*

At the hospital, they ran some blood tests and checked me over fully, including urine samples, to ensure everything was okay with my body. The nurse also removed a few small pieces of glass from my forearms. As I lay in the bed waiting for the all-clear, I asked one of the hospital staff if there was anything I could have to eat, as I was ravenous. I hadn't eaten anything since breakfast, and my appetite was off the charts. After a few moments, she brought me a salad sandwich, which I devoured within about a minute, pausing momentarily to laugh out loud at a piece of capsicum that fell out and looked exactly like a penis and testicles.

I returned normal blood tests, and physically everything was okay. Apart from the shock I felt, I had minor aches and pains and mild whiplash. The staff were happy for me to leave the hospital. Herein lay another challenge. I had no mode of transport to take me back to the Halls Gap Holiday Park, nor did I know anyone who could come and collect me from the hospital.

"Is there anyone working here that is heading out towards Halls Gap that may be able to drop me off?" I asked the nurse. She went to check, but no one was heading out that way. After the forty-five-minute taxi ride back to Halls Gap, we arrived at the holiday park. I looked at the taxi meter, which read $170. I let the driver know I didn't have any money on me and I didn't know where all of my things were. I offered to transfer the money in the morning. The taxi driver began to write the bank details on a scrap of paper, before scrunching it up and turning to me. "I think you've had a big enough day already, love. Don't worry about the fare." Once again, I was touched by the generosity of the human spirit, and the kindness shown by these people I'd never met before.

It was the dark of night by the time we arrived back at Halls Gap. I walked to the reception and collected the key from the small wooden box. A warm yellow light glowed in the entrance of the small cabin that Clementine had put aside for me. At the front door lay my suitcase, its royal blue colour difficult to make out through the thick layer of dust covering it. I opened the door, walked in, undressed and got ready for a nice warm shower. I placed the clothes I was wearing, as well as the small backpack and its contents, on the floor, and took a photo on my phone as a reminder of how little I had with me that day in the bush. The tears flowed well into the stillness of the night as I recalled the events of the afternoon.

In the morning, I got dressed and made my way to the reception, where I met Clementine for the first time. I was struck by her natural beauty and shining eyes. We hugged and shared a few tears as I told her the story of what had happened the day before.

Over the next two days, Clementine and her family welcomed me into their lives. They fed me at their family table, took me to the local shopping centre to buy myself some essentials and supported me through the whole experience; making calls on my behalf, researching things for me and helping me to plan out what to do next. They were the angels I needed. They helped to bring me to my feet.

Twelve

Fine Print

The day following the accident, I phoned the van hire company to share with them what had happened. I listened in disbelief as the woman on the other end of the phone explained that the insurance package I'd purchased for around $1,500 AUD would not cover the accident. I didn't understand and exclaimed, "I bought insurance to cover me on this trip. What do you mean, it isn't covered?" In the fine print was a clause that states that you are not covered for a 'single vehicle rollover' and because there were no other cars involved, I was not covered under the current policy. I felt enraged as the woman ran through what would happen next. The vehicle would need to be towed at my expense to Melbourne, where the damage would be assessed. If it was deemed by the assessor to be beyond repair, or more expensive to repair than replace, I would be liable for the cost of a replacement vehicle.

Clementine was with me the morning of the call and could see when I reached a point where I could no longer participate in the conversation. With a fierceness, she took the phone out of my hands and roared down the line to the woman on the other end, reminding her there was a human being at the centre of all of this. Not once in our conversation had the woman asked me if I was okay. If I was well. If I'd been injured. She lacked the kind of empathy I felt was called for in a situation like this. Yes, it was my error for not reading the fine print properly, and I needed to own that. And yes, there were some details to be sorted. But there was also a person at the heart of the matter, who was in shock, and trying her best.

I was so overwhelmed by the phone call, and the actions required. I was probably not in the best state to have had the conversation so soon after the accident. I spoke with my mum and asked if she and dad could help me organise a tow truck to tow the van to Melbourne, where it would be assessed. Thank God for my mum and her strength of character. She took the reins, negotiated with the hire company, and stuck it to them when required. When I told the story to people in the months and years that followed, I was able to laugh about this moment. The moment of finding out I wasn't covered, referring to it as the '$1,500 not covered for anything package'. Not reading the fine print, that was my bad, but I also learned that single vehicle rollovers in high-top vans are very common. Perhaps a more important question to ask would have been: "What am I not covered for?" Lesson learned.

After three days at the holiday park, it was time for me to travel to the airport and then fly home on a flight booked by my mum. Obviously, I had no mode of transport and no idea how I was going to get there. Once again, the generosity of the human spirit shone through. Clementine's father, who I had never met before, drove me three hours to Ballarat. From there, I caught a bus to Melbourne. My mum organised for me to stay the night at the Holiday Inn, which was a short walk to the terminal. I went to my cool, air-conditioned room, set down my things and ordered room service while I ran the bath. I spoke with my parents and told them I'd arrived at the hotel safely and would see them in the morning.

The following day, I arrived at the Gold Coast airport and into the safety and comfort of my parents' arms. I was exhausted and perhaps still in a state of shock. It wasn't until I'd spent a few days at home that my body really started to ache, and I started to physically feel it all. The muscles in my neck and back were extremely tense and tight, and the rest of me felt heavy and lethargic. I rested a lot.

As the months rolled on, I heard nothing from the hire company about the accident or the vehicle being assessed. One month, nothing. Then two and three months passed, and still not a phone call or email from them. I wondered if they'd forgotten about it. I hoped they had. There was no way I was reaching out to them to remind them. During the fourth month, the very same day I had picked up a cheque from my lawyer for the settlement of my divorce from Trent—*the same day, I kid you not*—I received an email from the hire company. It read:

> Dear Jacqueline,
> Thank you for patiently awaiting further details regarding the single vehicle rollover that happened during your rental.
> Our claim costs are now finalised. The vehicle has been deemed a total loss by our Claims Handler. We now request the payment of $19,134.50 to settle this claim. Costs of the claim are detailed below, and attached is our proof of loss.
> If you are not able to pay this amount as a lump sum, please advise us so that we can arrange a payment plan.
> Please use your booking number xxxxx as the payment reference.
> Yours sincerely,
> Hire company

My initial reaction was something akin to shock. Shocked and disappointed, they'd remembered me. Shocked the vehicle was beyond repair and that they'd sent me a bill for just under $20,000 on the same day I'd got my divorce settlement. And to top it all off, they were requesting the lump sum payment be made within the month. Really?!

I spoke to my parents and a few close friends about what to do. I wondered if I should seek legal advice and try to challenge it, but then there was no guarantee that, after paying the legal fees, it would result in a positive outcome and the bill disappearing from my life. After a couple of weeks of sitting on it, I took matters into my own hands and wrote to the company advising them I didn't have the requested amount available, but that I could either transfer them a lump sum of $9,000, or I could pay the debt off at one hundred dollars per fortnight for as long as it took to settle the amount. I was attempting to call their bluff.

A few days later, I received a response from the company:

> Dear Jacqueline,
> Thank you for your email and your settlement offers.
> We would like to settle this matter outside of court, but neither of your offers is completely acceptable by us. The lump sum of $9,000 does not even cover half of our loss, and your payment plan of $100 per fortnight would take years to pay off our loss.
> However, I have spoken to our senior manager and was advised that the expectable figure for us is $12,000 as a lump sum and full and final settlement.
> Please advise your position regarding our settlement offer so that we can bring this matter to closure.
> Kind regards,
> Hire Company

I could see they were trying to bluff me right back. I wrote back and told them, as I previously did, that I didn't have that money to give to them as a lump sum. The best I could do at an absolute stretch was $10,000 as a lump sum, transferred this evening. Matter closed. Within an hour, I had a response from them agreeing to my final offer. I transferred the money that evening and exhaled a deep sigh of relief.

Thirteen

Seeking Solitude

About six months went by before I once again felt the urge to move, explore and venture out on my own. I was searching for an escape from living with my parents, from Malcolm and his tormenting games and from a career that was feeling unfulfilling. I'd been a loyal and dedicated employee for over seven years in my corporate role, but our small team had recently had a change in leadership, and despite my best efforts, I didn't vibe with our new manager. My own insecurities about my working ability and knowledge were at the heart of it. He brought a wealth of the textbook kind of management experience people find impressive. I, on the other hand, brought a different kind of knowledge and loved to be creative, think in ways others didn't and make connections. I judged these differences in our working styles and preferences. I judged myself and the contributions I made to the team. I doubted so much about myself and my abilities. I'd never felt like this previously, as I always felt seen and valued, whereas now I felt as though what I brought to the table didn't really meet the expectations of the new manager. Despite our differences, we got along well on the surface, but there was an underlying feeling within me that he didn't truly see all of me and appreciate my contribution. In turn, I began to question myself.

Each day that passed, I arrived at the office a lesser version of myself than I knew I could be. I lacked motivation for the work. It felt as though the projects I was given to work on were either the stuff no one else wanted to do, or things that were well and truly out of my capability, beyond stretch projects. Instead of having a conversation with my boss like a normal person would, I chose instead to take a walk through the garden of self-doubt. Nothing much grew there, except the seeds of my own sorrow and self-loathing, which I watered occasionally. I dragged myself out of bed each day, exhausted before I even stepped a foot out the door. My energy was low. I struggled to keep up with the daily grind. I didn't enjoy going to work anymore. I was craving something more. I just didn't know what that was. The discomfort and dislike I felt for my current set of circumstances eventually propelled me forward and into action. One of the most powerful ways I've found to gain clarity is to remove myself from situations and allow myself some time and space away from the thing to shine a light on what might need to change. I began searching for something to excite me once more.

One day while making myself a tea in the work kitchen, I had a conversation with a friend about my intentions to take a portion of the long service leave I'd accrued over the last seven years, telling him how I felt that some time away from the office would do me good. How I wanted to do something meaningful with the time I'd worked so hard for. I wanted to give to myself, while also helping others. In some of my darkest times, I'd found giving to others was one of the most powerful modes of healing. My body was telling me it was time. I was tired. I wanted to go to some beautiful quiet place where I could rest, restore, and lick the wounds of the last five years clean. He told me about a wellness retreat on the coast, one he had attended as a guest a few years prior. Their philosophy resonated deeply; rising and retiring with the sun, tai chi, moving every day in a variety of ways, organic food, spa treatments, saunas, a steam room, numerous hiking trails and accommodation nestled in amongst the beauty of the hinterland. The retreat offered a live-in volunteer program too, he told me. "You should check it out, see if it's a good fit."

I felt myself being drawn in more and more as he spoke about the place. A spark of curiosity ignited within. So, when I returned home from work that evening with a spring in my step, I was eager to find out more about the health retreat. I set down my bag, pulled out my laptop and began searching the internet. Within a few moments, I'd tracked it down. There in front of me were these incredible panoramic images of mother nature—the bush and the beach. The images alone were enough to instil a deep sense of peace and calm within me.

I scrolled through the site, searching for information on the volunteering opportunity, when I came across the contact details of the volunteer coordinator. I pasted her email address into a new mail message, completed the application, attached my resume and hit send, nervously awaiting a response. So much lay in the hope that this opportunity would eventuate. I needed this time. I needed a reset.

To my delight, I received a message back from her within a week. She explained in her email how popular the volunteering program was, with people travelling from all over Australia and internationally to participate. There was a waitlist I'd be added to, and if deemed a good fit, I would progress to a video interview with the volunteer coordinator. This process, she explained, could take a few months from when the application was first received, so I was asked to sit tight.

I found myself regularly checking my inbox in the weeks following our initial contact, hoping to see an email from them. A week passed, then another, and another. A whole month passed before I heard anything back. It came by way of an email offering me a six-week live-in placement beginning in May—in two months. I responded immediately with pure joy and excitement. At last, I had something to look forward to, an escape and a place to be with my thoughts once more.

In the lead-up to my time at the retreat, I made a pact with myself to use my time there wisely. I made a promise and commitment to take deep care of my mind and body, to heal the wounds I'd sustained through the last five years, to grieve the loss of many things: the parts of myself that no longer existed, the parts I missed and longed for, my beautiful son, my marriage with Trent, my beliefs about life itself. My goal was to return to a state of mental and physical strength and wellness, to come back to myself and reclaim my own power. After the six weeks, I wished to leave through those gates more connected to myself than I was when I arrived.

Those couple of months prior to getting there felt pretty intense. It was as if everything in my life ramped up, as if life itself was illuminating even more of the unseen parts to be healed. It felt like a pretty big deal. I placed so much emphasis on 'getting there' and would often catch myself saying things like, 'When I get there, I will...' Each day, I placed more pressure and expectation on myself to get there, to be better, to do better. I had an expectation that life would be better then. That the space and time I was giving myself would equate to a deep healing of many things. The pressure continued to build as time went on.

And then the day came. It was time to begin the next adventure. To set off on a quest of deep healing. I arrived at the retreat in my Mitsubishi Lancer, full of hopes, nerves and expectations. Beads of sweat formed on the palms of my hands as I turned into the driveway. I reached over and wound down all of the car windows, allowing the freshness of the crisp hinterland air to flow through the car. I was so used to driving on the highway, surrounded by traffic with the car windows up and air-conditioning on. If I ever did wind down the window, the air I breathed in was heavily polluted by the many cars and trucks travelling the roads with me. The air here was different. There was a freshness to it. It was as if with each inhale, the air I breathed was restoring me to a state of peace and tranquillity. I sat there for a few moments, the car in idle at the bottom of the driveway as I breathed deeply and began to slow down for the first time in many months.

The driveway was a steep 1.2km, and it was seemingly impossible to pick up any kind of speed as I climbed. I put the car into first gear and began the ascent. There were times I wondered if my little silver sedan would make it to the top. She rumbled and growled at me as the driveway grew steeper and we neared the retreat. Alternating between first and second gear, with the occasional prayer in between, we arrived at what felt like basecamp. I was greeted by a very friendly volunteer who showed me around and took me up to the accommodation. The volunteers all lived together in a lodge on the property. In comparison to the guests' accommodation, ours was very basic living, but we didn't care. Each of us was happy and grateful to have somewhere to stay. We were given our own bedroom with a single bed, free-standing clothes hanger and a few metal baskets to store our belongings. There were three bathrooms in the lodge, which meant we shared with one other person during our time there. I was totally fine with this arrangement.

For both guests and volunteers, the first afternoon is mostly spent unpacking and settling into the accommodation. There is also some time set aside for the guests and volunteers to explore the property and bask in all of its beauty before the 'official program' begins. Once I'd unpacked my things, I ventured out and began to explore. There were several walks and hiking tracks set out on the property, all of which I wanted to see as soon as possible. I chose a gentle walk out to the lookout to begin. I wandered along the grassy track, following it for about fifteen minutes before it opened up to the most magnificent view of the valley. I stood there in awe at the panoramic views of the lush green trees, black cockatoos calling to one another as they flew overhead and home for the evening, and most impressive, the colours painting the horizon as the sunset.

The walk to the lookout became an afternoon ritual most days. It was my way of connecting with nature and with myself. I almost always walked it alone, without the distraction of a phone with music or a podcast to divert my attention away from myself. This was my time to restore. I loved the way the light and the colours changed from day to day. Some days, there was a smear of soft pinks across an otherwise uninterrupted blue sky, and other days the reds and oranges were so vivid I could've sworn there was a volcano erupting on the horizon.

That first afternoon, I returned to my room and felt unwell, as if I was going to be sick, everything I'd consumed during the day swirling around inside of me like dirty clothes in a wash cycle. I stood up and ran to the bathroom. I was sure I was going to see an organ in the toilet bowl. One of the other volunteers alerted the volunteer coordinator, who came to the lodge to check on me. As we talked, she shared with me how very common it was for guests and volunteers to have the experience of chundering on the first day up the mountain. "There can be so much anticipation, and hype felt in the lead-up to arriving," she said, "and once you get here, it's like your body feels that it's safe to let it all go." I suppose it depends on your belief system, but I knew I was arriving at the retreat with a lot of baggage—most of it was emotional trauma from the past few years—so her explanation resonated with me. Once I had time to reflect on the experience and the weeks, months and years leading up to my arrival, I wasn't at all surprised I had such a physical reaction on my first day. It was the first and last time I would be sick in my six-week stay. I was grateful to get it all out on day one. Nailed it.

The retreat is prestigious and very well-known in Australia and across the globe. Guests invested a lot of money in themselves to stay here, and like us volunteers, they were called to the place for a variety of reasons. Some, to heal their emotional wounds, others, to recover from physical illness and ailments. And others who came for a reprieve from the intensity of their daily lives. Perhaps CEOs of corporations, people in the spotlight who needed some downtime and privacy, or everyday people in search of some rest and relaxation. People from all walks of life were welcome here, and I loved that about the place.

I was often intrigued by the way people showed up at the retreat. Some were so unwell when they arrived that they couldn't help but feel healed by the time they left. Others were so used to leading busy lives that, when they paused after such a long time of never stopping, their bodies saw this as permission to be unwell. Some guests spent five days out of their seven-day retreat in bed, unwell and unable to fully participate. At times it felt challenging to be around such sick and exhausted people as I had my own stuff to deal with too. People often came to me to share their life stories, or the story of what had led them to the retreat. Listening without judgement or concern for the human standing there in front of me wasn't always easy. Stories of incurable disease, abuse, addiction, and unfulfilling relationships were some of the more common themes that emerged in these conversations. Though it felt overwhelming at times, it also reminded me of our humanness, and I was grateful they found a way to bring voice to their deepest truths.

It wasn't all heavy, though. By far, my favourite part of every retreat was watching as the guests emerged at the end of their seven days with a warm glow, ready to re-enter the 'real world' more rested than when they'd arrived.

Fourteen

Volunteering

A day in the life of a volunteer varied from week to week and this was something I really enjoyed. I loved having lots of different things to do, many of them new experiences for me to immerse myself in, which excited me. Although we had variety in our daily tasks, we did a few consistent things each day to ensure the guests were comfortable and had everything they needed.

Wakeups

This was one of the best tasks from my perspective. We would get up early (around 5:00am) when it was still very dark, and really cold in winter, and walk door-to-door, knocking and waking up each guest by calling out their first name. The purpose of this activity was to ensure the guests were awake with enough time to have their warm morning drink and join the leads for the morning walk, which began each day at around 6:30am. There was a fair amount of ground to be covered with guest quarters spread all over the property, so we had a system in place whereby we split the circuit in half to ensure everyone was up on time.

After we'd woken the guests, we would head down to the meeting point and get the warm drinks prepared and set up morning activities. Each day, the guests had a choice as to what their day would look like—there were always two choices for every walk and activity. Yang was strenuous, designed to generate heat in the body and to get them sweating. Yin was a gentle approach if they felt they needed to slow down and greet the day with a slower, more nurturing vibe.

I enjoyed hiking along with the guests. Not only did I get the chance to talk to people, but I loved the more challenging walks as they really were sweat-inducing, and I always felt like I'd worked physically hard, which set me up for a great day. I also loved the gentle walks as they provided the opportunity to connect with the guests on a personal level and understand what brought them to such a beautiful place through their stories.

Kitchen

Being a mad foodie, I loved helping in the kitchen. We were given what some would perceive as the 'shit jobs'—two-hour shifts to help with things like peeling and chopping vegetables, making smoothies and juices, and rolling bliss balls. While these jobs might seem monotonous to some, I had the best time in the kitchen! I got along well with the chefs, and I loved learning about organic produce and watching them turn it into the most delicious dishes. We always had a good laugh on the kitchen shift.

The retreat took a communal approach to meals, with all meals shared in the guest dining room, together. If someone was unwell or struggling in some way, we were able to deliver food to their room, though this was rare.

The volunteers also had their own much smaller dining room, where we shared meals around a large square timber table. There were seven of us at any one time taking a place at the table. There were always new people coming in and out of the volunteering program, which sometimes made things interesting. Things were rarely hostile. Mostly, I felt that we formed a strong bond when we were there and were able to laugh and indulge. The real treat was venturing off the property after a hard day's work or on our days off. One time, we jumped in the car, drove to the beach to have an ice cream and watched the full moon rise over the ocean. Something so simple brought so much joy to our group—the pleasure of eating an ice cream after not having consumed sugar in over a month felt indulgent and deeply satisfying. And sometimes, it was the freedom we felt in driving out of the gates and choosing what our day looked like rather than having to follow the planned schedule.

Garden

The property had the most beautiful organic fruit and vegetable garden, which was maintained by two onsite gardeners with help from the volunteers. There were citrus trees scattered throughout the property, but we rarely tended to them.

Our role in the garden was to help with harvesting (mostly greens for the salads) and weed out the nutgrass, which was a major pest in the retreat gardens. For those who have no idea what nutgrass is, you are not alone! I didn't either. On the surface, it looks like normal grass; green spikey strands poking up throughout the garden beds. That is, until you dig a little, and find a root, connected to a small ball-bearing-sized nut, which is connected to another, and another, and another. Sometimes they'd be connected by a strand a metre long! Weeding nutgrass was a job I did not enjoy. It was labour-intensive and physically hard on the body as we'd be out in the sun, kneeling or squatting for up to four hours.

What surprised me the most in the beginning was that each evening, after having spent half a day in the garden, I would return to the lodge emotional. There was some sort of deep healing that occurred as I dug through the dirt, searching for weeds. It was as if I was mirroring this within, tending to my own internal garden, pulling out the weeds and turning the soil to encourage new growth.

Changeover day

Retreats ran one after the other with a morning in between to give the place a makeover before the next lot of guests arrived in the afternoon. What I loved about changeover day was definitely driving the golf buggies around the property. I had never driven a buggy before, so learning how to use them was so much fun. In the morning, we would bring all of the buggies down to the wash bays and give them a good clean before parking them in the sun to dry. Changeover days always had a nice vibe—the excitement of welcoming a new bunch of people and getting to know them. We'd also have the chance to welcome any new volunteers joining the group.

What I didn't enjoy about changeover day was the mammoth task of bringing all the suitcases and bags to and from the reception area. Essentially, we became porters for a few hours. Some guests packed lightly—one bag, minimal fuss (thank you, I love you). Others had enough luggage for the whole group. I had a good laugh the day I joined the cleaners to help with turning the rooms around. The retreat had a strict policy on no outside food or substances being brought in. This particular guest, whose room we were cleaning, had a suitcase wide open, full of all kinds of snacks and junk food. It reminded me of our humanness and that sometimes letting go of things we are addicted to can take time and practice.

I experienced a variety of new and different things during my time at the retreat, which was something I really loved. The standout moment was the day I suited up and tended to the bees. Tara, the resident gardener, kept a few hives on the property. These hives produced the most beautiful honey I'd ever tasted; super sweet, golden, thick, and lush. Tara was this radiant goddess of a woman, in her fifties, but didn't look a day over thirty-five. She glowed a summer bronze, her smile like a permanent tattoo forever beaming. Tara got around in her gardening get-up and cowgirl hat. She was always chirpy and seemed to be in a permanent state of joy. Unsurprisingly, she was a guest favourite, and one of my personal favourites too.

Early one morning, Tara approached me and said she had a special job she wanted me to help her with. I said yes immediately, with no insight or understanding into what I was signing myself up for. I just had a feeling it would be fun. She led me through a forest of citrus trees to a small garden shed. In the distance, I could see bee hives. Then she handed me a beekeeper's suit and helped me to pull it on. I don't remember the weather forecast that day, but it was a scorcher, even more so once I was fully suited up and ready to go. It was so hot that I had sweat pouring out of everywhere; boob sweat, bum sweat and everything in between. Not a glamorous job, but an important one.

Tara explained to me what we were there to do: check on the hives and replace some of the inside wooden frames. I'd never done anything like this before, and despite the initial feeling of excitement, I grew a little anxious. I kept asking her if there was any way the bees could enter my suit and sting me. "Nah, you'll be alright. This will stop them," she said, and with that, Tara got some duct tape and taped it around my wrists as if she were about to bind and gag me. It made me laugh, but the reprieve from my anxiety was momentary.

As Tara began to pull on her own suit, she said, "Oh, Jax, now I need to tell you I am anaphylactic to bees."

"You're fucking kidding me, aren't you?" I replied.

"Haha, no, darl, dead set allergic, but don't worry, I never get stung by my bees. I'll show you why."

I replied nervously, "Okay, where is your EpiPen, just in case anything happens?"

"I don't have it with me," she replied. "It'll be sweet, darl."

At that point, the temperature in my suit felt like it'd reached boiling point. Sweat poured out of me as I thought about Tara being stung by bees and dying a painful death, with me having no idea how to help. Tara gathered a few more items, including some wood chips, which she scattered into a small metal device resembling a kettle. She ignited the chips, and we walked over to the hives, a trail of smoke following us and alerting the bees to our presence. I could hear the hum of the bees at work, the occasional bee flying close, curious as to what we were doing there. Tara told me she believed the reason she didn't get stung by her own bees was because of the rapport she had with them.

"Hello, beautiful," I heard her say as the occasional bee buzzed around us. "Now, before I open any of the hives, I spend a few minutes meditating on the hive. We will do this together in a minute. What you might notice is that the bees behave differently from hive to hive. What is important for you to remember is that we are here to do a job, and these bees have a job to do also."

Tara prepared me for what was to come, explaining her process and what I could expect.

"The first thing that will happen when I open this hive is the guard bees will come and start buzzing around us. Sometimes they will fly into your face netting. Sometimes they will buzz around. It's important to keep calm as they do this. Breathe and remember, they are here to do a job. They're just protecting their little hive. But first, let's meditate on the hive".

As we stepped up to the first hive, I was intrigued as to what she meant by 'meditating on the hive'. It seemed a bit out there, even for me, but I was open to all experiences and waited to be led by her. Tara guided me to push my stomach up against the hive and to rest my hands, palms down, on top of the lid. She asked me to close my eyes and take some deep breaths from deep down in my stomach.

"This is how we communicate with the bees and let them know we are here and that it's okay", she said.

I noticed the vibration coming off the hive. It was a powerful sensation to feel. As I stood there with my stomach resting against the hive, I could feel the bees, and it was as if my body began humming along with them. I don't know if I've ever felt as connected to myself, or to nature as I did in that moment. After a few deep breaths, Tara lifted the lid and *bang!* The first guard bee flew right into my face cover and scared the absolute shit out of me. I began to swat it away with my hand in sheer panic that it might enter my suit and sting me. Tara reminded me to keep calm and remember they were doing their job. She told me to breathe and focus on the job we were there to do. And as if through some kind of magic, with each breath I took, my body relaxed, and the bees did too; no longer intimidated by my presence nor I of theirs.

At a guess, it took ten minutes per hive to change over the frames. Just as Tara had explained, every hive was different, which was incredible to me. The first couple were calm and uninterested in what we were doing, followed by one very angry bunch who were not overly keen on us disturbing them. We replaced a few wooden frames before returning to the shed to take off our suits. I am pleased to tell you Tara lived to see another day.

The volunteers had one or two scheduled days off per week, in which we could either join in on the program along with the guests or do our own thing. I loved participating in the retreat activities. Dancing has always been a love of mine, and I discovered a deeper love for it while staying at the retreat. They offered a dance class a couple of times a week. What I loved about it was that there was a loose structure as well as the opportunity to 'free dance'. Dancing was another way in which I was able to feel grief and move it through my body, sometimes in steps that were graceful and elegant, and other times, it was wild and free.

On the evenings that I didn't walk to the lookout, I'd spend time in the steam room, alternating every few minutes between the heat of the steam and a cool shower. The steam room wasn't an overly popular place in the late afternoon, so volunteers used it as a space to catch up and unwind. We'd often share a laugh or catch up on any kind of drama that unfolded throughout the day. Plus, there was the added benefit of it being situated within the day spa, so we used it as an excuse to enjoy the luxury of the soft white linen, long warm showers and the organic products on our skin. It was such a treat to go there a couple of afternoons a week and indulge the senses.

My six weeks as a live-in volunteer was nearing the end, and I had mixed emotions about what this meant for me. After having lived in such a beautiful, nurturing environment for so long, with organic food prepared and served up three times a day and gentle practices incorporated, I wondered which of these I could sustain, and which ones would fall away. Eventually, I had to return home, and then go back to work.

My first day in the office was underwhelming, set off by the fact that someone else was sitting at my desk. As I walked up, my work mate said, "Oh, Jax, you don't sit there anymore. Your desk is there now." She pointed to a cardboard box resting on an otherwise empty work area. I don't know what it was about this specific situation, but it triggered me, and I turned to walk away. I could see they had good intentions, and there was probably a valid and logical reason for the move, though it made me feel as if they didn't care about me as a human. I'd loved my previous spot, window view and all. I'd been in the team for a really long time, and we'd always talked about stuff like that. Yet here I was, first day back in the office after experiencing seven weeks of bliss out in nature, only to be welcomed back to find my shit packaged up in a cardboard box and put to the side. Not the welcome I'd expected.

It took a little while to get over myself and accept the change of scenery, but I got there eventually. It also took some time to reintegrate back into the corporate world again after having lived like a hippie in the mountains for almost two months. It wasn't long before the manager, who I found awkward, took another position with a different organisation, and I was teamed up with a new employee who'd joined while I was on leave. I was immediately struck by her warmth and kindness. Over the three or so years that followed, we formed a strong working relationship and friendship. We created magic together in the projects we collaborated on. We were a great team. I felt excited, and I began to trust myself again.

And with that, many other things began falling into place around me.

I relocated to the coast after finding a small granny flat to live in. It was time for me to be free again, to have a space for myself and to move out of my parents' home. I felt ready. I craved alone time. I wanted a place of my own again to decorate and make sacred for myself. It would also be the beginning of the process of letting go of *him*.

Once and for all.

Fifteen

Cutting
Ties

I knew it was time to tackle the Malcolm problem. Everything else in my life felt good, as if all the previously scattered pieces of the puzzle of my life had slowly made their way back together. I could see myself again. The ripples in the water now settled, and no longer reflected a distorted image of who I was. There was just the thing with him.

I was done with the relationship—or whatever it was—and with tormenting myself. I'd returned to a state of being where I was recognising myself once more. I was beginning to love myself again and was no longer willing to allow him to have any kind of control over me. This time felt different to all of the other times before when I had intended to cut all ties to him, because I knew I was ready. I could feel it. I'd made many attempts prior to free myself from the chains of Malcolm, but I don't think I was ever truly ready to let go, despite knowing and feeling how horrible it was to be in it. I resented him for the things he'd done and for the abuse he projected towards me. Yet I held the most resentment for myself for having stayed in a situation I knew was not right for me. I judged myself for letting it go on for so long and for losing sight of who I was, for having given away all my internal power to another person. I worked hard to resolve this within me. I needed to free myself of the resentment I carried and held in my body. I needed to forgive myself for losing my way because of the relationship.

Every person in my life who knew of him and who knew me had encouraged me time and time again to let go. Only a couple of my close friends and family had actually met him, as there was always a reason why a face-to-face couldn't happen, but many people in my life knew him through my sharing of the situation. They questioned me over and over about what I was doing this for, how it was serving me to stay in something so toxic and all-consuming, but like heroin to an addict, I was addicted to the drug that was this man. The highs were intoxicating, leaving me feeling as if I was floating on a cloud in a distant universe. And the lows were just as powerful, sending me into a darkness and depression so painful and so uncomfortable that I didn't want to stay there for too long. I would emerge from those lows with a thirst for the next high.

For any outsider looking in, it would have been easy to judge me and assume I wouldn't follow through on my promise and commitment to end the torment and break the cycle of abuse once and for all. I can understand why. Every other time, I doubted my own ability to let go and move on. I knew I wanted to, but I was riddled with worry, which, of course, prevented me from taking any action to move forward without him.

To get a different result, I needed to do things differently. I put a plan in place to help me with letting go. I knew it would take work. I knew it would challenge me at times. After all, being with this man was an addictive habit that needed breaking. And so, I treated it as if it were one, surrounding myself with the people and things that supported my letting go, and putting myself into my own form of rehabilitation.

Letting go didn't happen overnight. It took time. I didn't go cold turkey either, as I felt that approach would've been too much of a shock to my system, which was already sensitive and overstimulated. I continued to talk to Malcolm while working through the things inside of me that were keeping me from moving forward without him. I worked with a counsellor and a hypnotherapist. I read books and researched co-dependency and domestic violence. I wrote about the kind of man and life partner I wanted to attract into my life. About what was okay and not okay in a relationship. About how I wanted to be treated. I visualised myself as happy and content. I became obsessed with focusing on the type of relationship I wanted; both with myself and with another.

Of all the work I did, the most important was the work I did on loving myself through it all. Though I had an internal desire to act and do the work that felt big and hard, I also wanted to be gentle with myself as I moved through the pain and discomfort. I moved my body in all of the ways that helped me shift the grief and pain through and out. I knew how damaging it could be to keep it stored. It needed to move. I danced. I swam in the ocean and the fresh flowing waterfalls surrounding my home. I walked through the forests in the rain, my bare feet connected to the earth. Nature, ever the safe haven, the place I go when I am seeking, when my body is calling for rejuvenation—the place where all else falls away. A day in nature is an invitation into stillness and an opportunity to be truly alone with my thoughts and feelings. It's where I can truly feel it all, and then let it go. I sat in saunas and steam rooms until I felt the beads of sweat dripping down my body, releasing all the toxic energy I felt clogging up my pores. I wrote. I breathed deeply, deep into my stomach. I breathed like I hadn't for a long time—a full inhalation, a full exhalation, helping to slow my heart and restore me to a sense of peace.

Every song I played or audio I listened to was intended to make me feel good or support me as I walked the path of recovery. Only love and positivity went in. All else was unwelcome. I nourished and cleansed my body with beautiful, fresh produce. I cooked for myself as if I was the most important guest at the dinner table. The acts of love and kindness I showed to myself during this time revealed to me the love I'd been searching for all along—the love of my own tender heart.

I've always been amazed at how quickly things can happen in life when my energy is focused so intensely on the outcome—be it desirable or undesirable. Within the same month of beginning this work to let Malcolm go, another man entered my life. I judged this to be completely chance and out of the blue, at a time when I did not feel ready for any kind of relationship after what I'd endured with Malcolm.

A friend had organised a girls' night in at one of our girlfriends' places, followed by a day of op shopping. For whatever reason, come the afternoon, I didn't feel like driving up to Brisbane for the night and instead chose to stay at home. I lived just over an hour away and decided I'd meet them in the morning for breakfast before heading out to bag a bargain at the local op shops.

As the afternoon drew to a close, I received a message from a friend who lived just around the corner from me. Her cousin was up from Tasmania, and they were going to head out to a local food market for some dinner. In her exact words, "It'll be a cheap and early night." Feeling rather uninspired by the contents of my fridge and pantry, I decided I'd join them.

The night market was full of the kind of hustle and bustle you'd find in the busy streets of Asia. Food stalls were scattered throughout a huge undercover area nestled in the back streets of suburbia. We listened to live music as we ate, drank, and laughed. I decided I'd be the designated driver for the night as I didn't really drink a lot of alcohol anymore, anyway. Once we'd finished our food, my friend was keen to 'kick on,' and I agreed to take them wherever they wanted to go. We went on what I would describe as a mini pub crawl around Burleigh Heads until we ended up at the casino at midnight. We met and hung out with a bunch of dads from Melbourne who were on a night out. They were such gentlemen and lots of fun. I ended up having a deep and meaningful conversation with the designated driver from their group.

It was about 3am when I hit the dance floor, still completely sober, with my friend. She'd been talking on and off with a fellow who, from what I could see, was out with a group of his friends for the evening, all of whom were extremely intoxicated.

And then there he was.

He was very clearly intoxicated, swaying as he spoke. Usually, I find drunk men repulsive and do not afford them much of my time. When they're unable to speak or string words together, I am out. Yet there was something about him, enough for me to stay and talk. We spoke for a little while and then drifted off to be with our friends, re-connecting throughout the morning at the bar, or on the dance floor to talk some more.

Out of nowhere, and mid-conversation, he asked me for my phone number. Initially, I was taken aback as I am very rarely approached by men in this way. I think it's the resting bitch face I so often take with me on nights out! "I don't really know anything about you," I replied. "Like, where are you from?" He told me he was there with his friends on a buck's weekend. They were all from Tamworth, about six hours from where we were. Tamworth was a little far away for me, and I said as much. He explained that they'd grown up together in Tamworth, but he lived on the Gold Coast. My interest piqued a little, so I asked him to rate his level of drunk on a scale of one to ten, one being sober and ten being paralytic. He responded with a nine. So, when I finally gave him my phone number and watched him search for the letters to spell out my name like a person who'd never seen a keyboard in their life, I had truly no expectation of ever hearing from him again. And I was completely and wholeheartedly okay with that. I took the phone and typed in my name and number. If I heard from him, I heard from him. If I didn't, I didn't. Either scenario was okay with me.

Two days later, and to my great surprise, I woke to a message from him with a request to meet for a drink and a chat. Again, with no real expectations of anything at all and feelings of intrigue coursing through my body, I said yes. We met the following week for a walk along the beach. I did most of the talking, while he listened. We spoke about lots of different things and dove deep in conversation for a first meeting. I was surprised and delighted by his ability to talk about these things. It felt calm. It felt nice. There were no feelings of pressure or expectation. It felt like nothing more than two people sharing a conversation about their lives.

We walked to the rock wall and talked some more before deciding to head back. By this time, I was starving for dinner, having met him straight after a long day of work. I invited him to join me if he was hungry—no pressure. I was going to eat. If he was hungry, he could too. We went to the surf club before calling the night to a close. He offered to walk me to my car, which I thought was lovely, and highly unnecessary, though he insisted.

I smile when I remember that moment we said goodbye at the car. I am a notoriously awkward human, especially in situations like a first date. I often say things that are cringe-worthy and weird. It's just how I roll. "I really don't know how to wrap this kind of thing up," I said. "Neither do I." "How about a fist bump?" He smiled and agreed. And with that, we reached out a clenched fist to the other, bumped knuckles and went our separate ways.

I phoned my friend when I got home. She was anticipating my call to give her a review of the date and also to reassure her I hadn't been abducted by this man I knew nothing about. "He is a really nice man," I summarised. "But I spent most of the time talking. He seems really quiet and maybe a little bit shy. But there is something about him. I am intrigued." "Do you think you will catch up with him again?" she asked. "I will wait and see what happens. If he wants to meet again, I'm open to it." "Did you kiss?" she asked. "Of course not!" I exclaimed. "I created one of those awkward moments, and we bumped knuckles."

We broke into fits of laughter.

We met a couple more times in the weeks that followed. I began to have all the thoughts flood my head. I told myself over and over the timing of meeting this man wasn't right. It wasn't right according to whatever timeframe and schedule I had placed on myself. I wasn't ready to jump into a new relationship or for any kind of commitment. There was an undeniable feeling of something wonderful beginning to emerge between us. We had this lovely balance of spending enough time together to get to know one another, while also dedicating time to our own lives and the things we loved.

And I suppose, in a way, it all felt so great that it almost felt too good to be true, and so I questioned it all. He entered my life at a time when wounds were being healed, a time when I was laser-focused on myself, on getting well, on overcoming the many obstacles that previously stood in my way, and on doing more of the things I loved. I was receiving support to assist me in freeing myself from what felt like a deep entanglement to Malcolm.

And then I would pause and remind myself to slow down, to take each moment as it came and for what it was. I reminded myself that some people enter our lives in these moments of navigating through the end of a relationship as if some kind of guiding light to show us the way out. They are there to provide us moments of ecstasy and intimacy, nourishing us in ways that will sustain us through our transition out of a relationship and into life. They stay for as long as required—sometimes a moment, a month, a year and sometimes, if meant for us, they stay for a lifetime. Who knew what this would become? Maybe something beautiful. Maybe not. *One step at a time, Jacqueline.*

The day I shared with Malcolm that I'd met a man, he completely lost his mind, unable to cope. He was hysterical and screaming down the line. I caught it and recognised the abuse, rage and anger being projected towards me. This time I was different in how I chose to respond. There was a calm within me. I took some deep breaths and let him go on for a few minutes. The threat of suicide came once again as he continued firing abuse, blame and judgement towards me. Instead of being fearful and seeing it as something that could be my fault if he did follow through, I said very calmly, "What you choose to do from here is your choice. It has nothing to do with me. I am moving on with my life, moving forward. I suggest you do the same." The hysteria rose to another level after that, with the threats of suicide continuing. I chose to hang up the phone.

I didn't need to endure his abuse any longer. I was shaking as I ended the call, though there was a sense of peace knowing I wouldn't be seeing this man ever again. For the first time in a long time, I felt empowered and strong. I knew there would not be another ounce of my energy invested. I contacted his mother, who was overseas at the time, and shared the situation with her. For the first time, I told her about the threats he'd made to kill himself. I asked her to contact him and to be his support, as it wasn't up to me to take care of him anymore, or to stress about his actions and decisions. She was understandably upset and concerned for her son. It probably also didn't help that she had no real understanding of the actual relationship we'd had. I handed over the baton. I had to keep moving forward. It was done. I wouldn't be returning.

A couple of weeks later, I returned home from work to a ten-page handwritten letter in a box along with a handful of printed photos of us and a few small keepsakes. *Fuck me.* I sat down and prepared myself. As soon as I unfolded the pages I realised the intentions behind it. Pages littered with blame and shame and a clear lack of personal responsibility from his part. He judged my choices, my morals and ultimately who I was as a woman. *That's enough now, Jacqueline. You have suffered and punished yourself enough already. This man no longer has any power over you. Put the letter down.* I tore it into a thousand pieces.

On this path of cleansing and clearing things out, I went through my wardrobe, my wallet, and my whole house, systematically collecting every item that triggered any memories. I gathered them—diamond necklace and all—and took them outside to the bin along with the letter. I needed to fully let go of everything.

When writing this book, I sat down with my mother to share with her my intentions. For the first time, I told her the story about the termination. We spoke at length about the relationship and what it was like for me, and for them as my parents, witnessing their daughter suffering.

During that conversation, Mum shared with me that he had written her and Dad a letter too, which she would show me if I wanted to read it. I had a moment of curiosity, but not enough to want to see it. What shocked me the most out of this whole conversation with my mother was not that they'd received a letter from him, and they'd kept it, but why they did. Curious, I asked her why.

"Jacqueline, your father and I said to each other that we would keep this letter forever. We wanted to keep it in case anything ever happened to you, you know, like if he killed you or anything."

My jaw hit the floor as I heard those words. Having been so caught up in it all, I hadn't considered the impact the relationship had on those closest to me. I had no idea my parents felt this way. In my mind, I'd done a fairly good job of hiding what was really happening. The revelation that they perceived him as this dangerous man who could potentially harm me was shocking. And I say shocking, not because I didn't agree with what I was hearing, but because perhaps I could see the truth in what they were saying. This conversation with my mother only further validated the decision I'd made to cut all ties to Malcolm.

With this desire to let go, also came the desire to shed another layer of grief I felt in my heart. So, on what would have been Jack's fifth birthday, I decided it was time to set Jack free and spread his ashes.

Sixteen

Letting Go

I wanted to remember this time in the years to come, and I felt compelled to capture the story in some way, so I reached out to a local photographer who I randomly found on a Google search. I'd never met her before. I shared with her my intentions to spread Jack's ashes over a river that Trent and I had spent a great deal of time at throughout our relationship and during my pregnancy. I explained how I wished to capture this part of our story visually. There was a warmth to her tone, a sense of safety and comfort in her words. In my heart, I felt she was the perfect person to support me through this process. All of this was confirmed when I met her. Grace was incredibly beautiful with long curly golden locks flowing, her voice soft and gentle. She felt like an angel sent from above.

Trent met me by the river where we took some photos together. This in itself was an interesting experience as we both were a little awkward in those initial moments on the shore, not really knowing how to do grief in this way. I wasn't at all surprised that we struggled so much in coming together and grieving, for this had been one of the major challenges in our relationship. Through the awkwardness we felt, we found a way. It came in the form of an outstretched hand, an embrace, a word of comfort or support. And together, we did what we were unable to do five years earlier. We held the space for the other to grieve in whatever way they chose, and it was one of the most beautiful experiences of my life.

Trent took the urn and had some time with Jack. He poured him out over the river and honoured him in his own way. I stood back as he did what he needed to do. Trent said goodbye and thanked me for including him before leaving me to have my time with Jack.

And here's the thing, in the lead-up to deciding I was ready to spread Jack's ashes, I hadn't considered Trent being a part of it. And that might seem heartless, but I knew he'd moved on with his life and had started his own family. Part of me felt as though I would be inviting him back into aspects of his life he might not want to revisit. I made a whole lot of assumptions about the situation and what he would or wouldn't want to do. I'd assumed I'd do it on my own, as I had been on my own for some time. In the days leading up to it, a beautiful man in my life encouraged me to include Trent in the process. "If I were Trent, and this was my child, I would want to be part of it all. Even if it was only a small part. I think it would be nice to ask him and let him decide."

I'd written to Trent and told him about my plans to spread Jack's ashes at one of our favourite places on the coast. I invited him and his new partner to be part of the celebration. To my surprise, Trent thanked me and agreed. Afterwards, he thanked me once more and shared that he may have been a bit upset and disappointed if I had not included him. It was a big experience for us both, and it was nice to share in another layer of letting go.

When Trent left, I felt I had the space to really feel it all. I embodied the process of grief and letting go in a way I wasn't prepared for. It called for a deeper healing than just watching him drift with the tide. In saying all of that, I had no plan. No process or any kind of pre-rehearsed steps to follow. Grace encouraged me to take as much time as I needed. To do whatever I felt guided to do, and that she would be there on the sidelines capturing the images for my memory.

My heart was open.

I breathed deeply.

I led myself very unexpectedly through an embodied journey of letting go, grief and re-birth. I walked into the water. Jack's tiny olive-coloured urn cupped in my hands. Selecting the urn was a decision I allowed our mothers when we were in the hospital. It was something that needed doing as our wish had been to have Jack cremated. I felt incapable of choosing the urn at the time, for many reasons, but mostly due to being both physically and emotionally depleted. Perhaps this was also my way of including our mothers in the process of letting go and inviting them to feel their own grief. After all, Trent and I weren't the only ones who excitedly anticipated the arrival of this baby. Many lives were impacted by the creation, the birth, and the death of Jack—our beautiful child.

Our mothers visited a local funeral garden and selected the olive-green urn with a golden trim around the top and bottom. They arranged to have it engraved, choosing an image of the tree of life for the front and centre. The tree's golden leaves glistened each time the light touched them. When our mums brought the urn to the hospital, the first thing that struck me was not its beauty and simplicity, but the size of it. It was tiny, no larger than a kitchen spice jar. I'd only ever seen the urns of adult humans or beloved family pets, and these were much bigger. "Is he in there? Like, he actually fits in there. It seems really small." They laughed. When I thought about it later, it made more sense. Of course, it was a tiny urn. He was a tiny human.

I poured some of the ash into my open palm, taking a moment to feel it in my hand. It was surprisingly coarse and grey in colour, fragments of bone scattered throughout. It was unlike the ash I knew, which was the soft ash of a campfire. I leaned down and carefully collected some salt water from the river with my other hand, allowing a few drops to fall and mix in with the ash. I took my index finger and blended them together until the mix resembled clay. I poured out more and more of him, continuing to mix him in with the water and spread him all over my hands, up my arms and over my face before running my fingers through my hair.

I walked further out into the water, pausing at times to rest my hands on my heart and to weep, at other times stopping to wash the clay from my body as if some kind of cleansing ritual was occurring. I bent down and began wetting the ends of my hair until it was soaked by the salt water. I twisted it around my fingers and wrung it out, repeating this process a few more times before taking some more steps out into the water. Now waist deep, wading through the water and being guided only by my heart, I stretched my arms out in front of me, took a deep breath and dove into the depths of the river. I was completely submerged in the water, wearing a long navy dress, feather earrings dangling. I was certainly not dressed for a swim, but I dolphin-dove under the water and floated on my back. My arms and legs spread like a star. My eyes gazing up at the beautiful blue sky. I spent a good hour in the water with Jack in this way.

My friend met me there with a wreath she'd made from various plants and flowers, a section of it made from an olive branch. One tiny little olive could be seen among the leaves. I saw this as an omen. I stood in the water with her and said a little prayer as we pushed the wreath away from us and watched it float down the river.

We walked back to the shoreline and thanked Grace for her time. Emerging from the water that day felt like the beginning of something new.

I walked out a little lighter than when I'd entered. I smiled.

My face glowed.

My eyes glistened.

I felt joy in my heart.

I felt happy and free.

I felt more me than I had in all the years prior to this moment.

I emerged from that water re-born.

As we walked to our cars, rain clouds began to roll in, covering the relatively uninterrupted blue sky. And then it began to pour.

Seventeen

A Chance Encounter

We fell in love. The man I met at the casino, Ryan is the exact man I had imagined myself with—country twang and all. I became a stepmother, welcoming a stepdaughter into my life. This was no easy task, taking on a parent role to a child who isn't my own, and I often struggled to find my way in the relationship with my stepdaughter in those early days. Initially, I thought I needed to love her as if she was my own child, until I realised it was okay that I didn't feel that same connection. Over time, we've found our way and have come to love each other in a unique and beautiful way to us.

Ryan and I had a child of our own. My experience of labour and birth with her was so beautiful. I wasn't sure how I would be entering into another pregnancy after Jack. *Might I be anxious or afraid that something might happen again?* I am glad I allowed myself the time to grieve for Jack in the way I did and to move the grief through my body. I believe the time, space and every other experience after his birth equipped me with an inner strength and courage to move through my pregnancy with relative ease and grace. That's not to say it was all smooth sailing. There were moments along the way where I felt anxiety and fear within me, most of which was during the third trimester. I'd never been that far along in any pregnancy and the thought of being so close to the birth of our child and something going wrong was terrifying. Excitement increased as I neared the day where my baby would be born. I was so close to meeting her and holding her in my arms. Yet I also felt tentative.

We paid for our own private obstetrician, who I visited when I was feeling fearful. He guided me through the big emotions and was great at giving me the science and facts to reassure me that all was well. I also downloaded and listened to a number of Hypnobirthing and Calm Birth audios, as well as daily birthing affirmations. Each space I regularly sat or stood in was littered with these affirmations, inspirational quotes, and positive birth stories. All the audio I listened to was full of the good stuff I wanted to feel. I did not allow the stories of other people's traumatic births to overshadow the clear vision I had of my birth being calm and beautiful. What is it with people sharing their birth horror stories with expectant mothers?

People laughed at me when I told them of my intention to have a calm birth. I received all the comments. 'Oh, just you wait until you're in there in pain. You won't have time to worry about a calm birth.' Others laughed at the cards I had up in my workspace and judged me in their own way. I realise now that 'My vagina is soft and open' is probably not the most appropriate affirmation card to be displayed in a corporate workspace!

And with my effort to create a calm and peaceful space within, I did it. We created the most beautiful birth experience for ourselves and welcomed a darling girl into the world. My heart opened and softened even more upon meeting her, and my love continues to deepen with each day we spend together. Watching the joy on her face when she sees her sister brings me an internal joy and comfort. I love my stepdaughter even more for the joy she brings to our daughter.

Our family dynamic is perfect in its own way. Not in the ways we've become conditioned to recognise as perfection—the prince riding in on the horse and saving the damsel in distress and them living happily ever after—but perfect in the sense that we are living out our own version of happily ever after. Sometimes life is challenging and messy, but if we look deep enough, there is such beauty and magic in the mess. We relocated as a family to a remote outback town and live a quiet and simple life in the bush.

As I look back over my life and the circumstances and situations that led me to this point, I do so with a grateful heart. I bow in gratitude to myself for finding the courage and bravery to overcome things I believed were impossible at the time, for adventuring into the unknown, and trusting my heart as the compass. For there, waiting patiently on the other side of every fear I ever had, were the most beautiful things I could never have imagined.

About the author

Jacqueline Gaul's writing illuminates the path of resilience and love. She is inspired by authenticity in a fake world and admires those who courageously embrace their true selves. A mother to two living children and one angel baby, Jacqueline explores a multipurpose life—from outdoor adventures and crystals to rap music. *The Overcoming: A Story of Resilience and Love After Loss* is her first book.

Milton Keynes UK
Ingram Content Group UK Ltd.
UKHW040826250224
438359UK00004B/192